Spon's Budget Estimating Handbook

OTHER TITLES FROM E & FN SPON

Commercial Estimator
Marshall & Swift

Construction Tendering and Estimating
J.I.W. Bentley

Estimating Checklist for Capital Projects
2nd Edition
Association of Cost Engineers

Project Management Demystified
Today's tools and techniques
G. Reiss

Residential Estimator
Marshall & Swift

Spon's Asia Pacific Construction Costs Handbook
Davis Langdon & Seah International

Spon's Construction Cost and Price Indices Handbook
B.A. Tysoe and M.C. Fleming

Spon's Contractors' Handbooks
    Minor Works, Alterations, Repairs and Maintenance
    Plumbing and Domestic Heating
    Painting, Decorating and Glazing
    Electrical Installation
Tweeds

Spon's European Construction Costs Handbook
Davis Langdon & Everest

Spon's Fabrication Norms for Offshore Structures
A handbook for the oil, gas and petrochemical industries
Franklin & Andrews

Spon's Price Books
    Architect's and Builders' Price Book
    Mechanical and Electrical Services Price Book
    Civil Engineering and Highway Works Price Book
    Landscape and External Works Price Book
Davis Langdon & Everest

For more information on these and other titles please contact:
The Promotion Department, E & FN Spon, 2–6 Boundary Row, London, SE1 8HN.
Telephone 071 865 0066.

Spon's Budget Estimating Handbook

Second edition

Edited by

Tweeds

(incorporating Spain and Partners)
Chartered Quantity Surveyors

E & FN SPON

An Imprint of Chapman & Hall

London · New York · Tokyo · Melbourne · Madras

Published by E & FN Spon, an imprint of Chapman & Hall, 2–6 Boundary Row, London SE1 8HN, UK

Chapman & Hall, 2–6 Boundary Row, London SE1 8HN, UK

Blackie Academic & Professional, Wester Cleddens Road, Bishopbriggs, Glasgow G64 2NZ, UK

Chapman & Hall GmbH, Pappelallee 3, 69469 Weinheim, Germany

Chapman & Hall Inc., One Penn Plaza, 41st Floor, New York NY 10119, USA

Chapman & Hall Japan, Thomson Publishing Japan, Hirakawacho Nemoto Building, 6F, 1–7–11 Hirakawa-cho, Chiyoda-ku, Tokyo 102, Japan

Chapman & Hall Australia, Thomas Nelson Australia, 102 Dodds Street, South Melbourne, Victoria 3205, Australia

Chapman & Hall India, R. Seshadri, 21 Second Main Road, CIT East, Madras 600 035, India

First edition 1990

Second edition 1994

© 1990 E & FN Spon

© 1994 Bryan Spain

Printed in Great Britain by T.J. Press (Padstow) Ltd, Padstow, Cornwall.

ISBN 0 419 19250 6

A catalogue record for this book is available from the British Library

Library of Congress Catalog Card Number available

Printed on permanent acid-free text paper, manufactured in accordance with ANSI/NISO Z39.48-1992 and ANSI/NISO Z39.48-1984 (Permanence of Paper).

Contents

Foreword

Estimates of the cost are needed at every stage through which construction projects pass. It is a worthy aim in construction project management that all significant decisions about design, construction and commissioning should be accompained by an estimate of the cost of each of the options being considered.

One paradox of construction project management is that the earlier the decision has to be made, the more difficult is the task of estimating the cost implications. When design has been done and specifications, sizes and quantities are known, the cost estimating can be detailed and relatively accurate. When little or no design has yet been done, estimating is very much more difficult.

Another paradox of construction project management is that the most important decisions are taken earliest - when the cost estimates are the most difficult to obtain.

These considerations lead to the conclusion that cost estimating data arranged particularly to suit the very early stages of a project - when the budget is being set - will be particularly useful yet particularly difficult to obtain. The difficulty of obtaining the data may be the reason why no book devoted entirely to budget estimating in construction has been prepared until this one.

Bryan Spain's team ranged widely to assemble the estimating data which this book contains. They have also thought carefully about the best way to arrange and present the data for budget estimating and written some purposeful and well informed commentary to help readers make best use of what is here.

Many projects will start on a firmer footing when the decision to go ahead is based upon the sort of estimate which this book will help managers to prepare.

Martin Barnes
Martin Barnes Project Management
Coopers & Lybrand Deloitte

Preface
to the second edition

This is the second edition of Spon's Budget Estimating Book. The first was published in 1990 and was welcomed by those people in the construction industry involved in the early stages of the financial planning of projects.

The person responsible for preparing an approximate cost of a project (usually a quantity surveyor) which has only progressed from an idea to a sketch drawing, is in a difficult position. Every instinct tells him (or her) to be cautious and not to proffer a figure until better information is available . But if the fee-paying client insists..... 'Just an idea... a ballpark figure... an approximation of costs will do' he will say. The hapless QS will reply 'OK, but I should have much more information, but if you insist, I think about £1.75 million'. 'How much?' the client will explode, 'it can't be. That's far too high'. And another project gets off to a bad start!

This book is intended to reduce this type of confrontation by providing cost information to match every stage of development of a project from sketch to detailed drawings.

I am grateful for the help I have received in the preparation of this book from many sources including many manufacturers and material suppliers. Thanks are also due to:

Darren Maxwell	John McGee
Paul Spain	Brendan O'Herlihy
Pentith Construction (Poynton)	Building Materials Market Research
Association of Consulting Engineers	Royal Institute of British Architects
Royal Institution of Chartered Surveyors	Water Research Centre
Building Costs Information Service	

I would welcome constructive criticism of the book together with suggestions for improving its scope and contents.

Whilst every effort is made to ensure the accuracy of the information given in this publication, neither the author nor the publishers in any way accept liability of any kind resulting from the use made by any person of such information. The prices in this book are based upon costs current in the last quarter of 1993.

Bryan J.D. Spain, FInstCES MACostE

TWEEDS (incorporating Spain and Partners)
Chartered Quantity Surveyors
Cavern Walks
8 Mathew Street
Liverpool L2 6RE

Preface
to the first edition

This book has been written for everyone in the construction industry who has an interest in budget costs. All projects start (and sometimes die!) as an idea and invariably the first question to be asked is 'How much will it cost?' At this stage a wide variety of methods are used to assess the approximate cost of construction.

The book contains a broad range of information to help the developer, quantity surveyor, engineer, architect or landscape architect produce costings to enable decisions to be taken on the feasibility and financial viability of the proposed scheme. The book has been divided into classifications of work i.e. building, civil engineering, mechanical and electrical, reclamation and landscaping and refurbishment and most projects will contain an element of more than one classification.

Various terms are used to describe the result of the cost assessment e.g. 'order of costs', 'approximate estimate', 'budget estimate' and others but they all have the same aim, to produce the most accurate financial forecast based upon the best information available. As further details are available the cost forecast should be upgraded and refined to match the changes so that the client has the best information available at any one time.

The authors have received help from many sources in the preparation of this book including the manufacturers of a wide range products. Other valuable help was received from:

Water Research Centre
Liverpool Polytechnic
Royal Institution of Chartered Surveyors
Building Cost Information Service
Association of Consulting Engineers
Royal Institute of British Architects
Association of Consultant Architects
Institute of Landscape Architects
Paul Young
Dorothy Spain
Carol Downham

Our thanks are also due to John McGee of Martin Barnes Project Management (Coopers & Lybrand Deloittes) who wrote the chapter on Life Cycle Costing, Brendan O'Herlihy of Chestertons for the chapter on the Development Process and Andy Williamson of Building Services Design who contributed the cost information on Mechanical and Electrical work.

We are particularly grateful to Denys Milton who carried out most of the detailed research necessary for the production of the thousands of individual pieces of cost information that appear in the book.

We would welcome constructive criticism of the book together with suggestions for improving its scope and contents.

Whilst every effort is made to ensure the accuracy of the information given in this publication, neither the authors nor the publishers in any way accept liability of any kind resulting from the use made by any person of such information. The prices in this book are based upon costs current in the first quarter of 1990.

Bryan J.D. Spain, FInstCES MACostE
Leonard B Morley, DipQS FRICS MInstCES MACostE

SPAIN AND PARTNERS
Consulting Quantity Surveyors
Unit 9
SMM Business Park
Dock Road
Birkenhead
Merseyside
L41 1DT

Introduction

The purpose of this book is to help in the preparation of budget
estimates at the early stages of a project. These budget costs must be
established at the feasibility stage to assess the projects viability and
different methods can be used to achieve this.

For building work, using square metre prices is usually the first
approach but the chapters on elemental costs and composite rates
should provide the reader with enough information to enable him to
upgrade the accuracy of the square metre prices where necessary.
Civil engineering, reclamation and landscaping work do not lend
themselves to the square metre method so information on principal
item and composite rates has been included. The scope and meaning
of these and other items is set out below.

Square metre prices

These give a selection of average costs per   square metre of buildings
based on the total floor area measured   inside external walls and over
all stairwells, liftwells, internal walls   and other voids. It should be
mentioned that these rates should be used only as a guide showing
differences between building costs rather than a measure by which
budget estimates could be calculated. Wherever possible approximate
quantities should be taken off to calculate budget estimates. In
building work the prices are inclusive of preliminary and general
items but do not include external works, equipment, furniture or fees
for professional services. Preliminary and general items costs vary
between 7% and 14% as a percentage size of the contract. Estimators
sometimes include part of the preliminaries cost in the individual
rates and the remainder in the preliminaries section of the bill of
quantities according to the methodology used by the contractor. The
actual value of the preliminaries in a contract is seldom less than
10%.

Elemental analyses

A selection of cost analyses of various types of buildings is stated
which should help the reader in preparing budget estimates from
sketch drawings.

Composite rates

These rates are most useful in budget estimating when applied to approximate quantities for the various elements of the building. The rates also enable comparisons to be made between the cost of different materials. The wide variation in the choice of materials available should enable the budget estimate to meet both the clients cost requirements and the design criteria.

   In civil engineering work Chapter 5, the rates pull together some of the items listed in Chapter 4 e.g. prices for concrete walls include formwork and reinforcement. This information will be useful when there is only time to prepare very approximate quantities. It will also help when comparing the costs of different sizes of walls.

Principal rates

The most frequently measured items have been selected with approximate rates set against them. These items and values could be used in   the preparation of budget estimates where there is enough time available to prepare and price rough quantities. In civil engineering work, the user must remember to include an allowance for Class A - General Items. This could be expressed as a percentage (say 25% to 40% depending upon the nature of the work) or could be assessed in detail by using the rates in Class A.

Project costs

This information is the most approximate in the book and gives an 'order of costs' for particular projects. It would normally be used when an overall idea of the costs was required rather than a budget estimate.

Examples in the use of the book are set out below using the information in the various chapters to calculate the budget cost of an entire project.

Example 1

Client requirements

1.	Factory:	single storey 2000 m2
2.	Office:	separate, two storey 400 m2
3.	Site:	10,000 m2
4.	Location:	East Anglia
5.	Siteworks:	sloping embankment on one side, 150 m of road from highway, car parking for 100 cars

From Chapter 1 - Building prices per square metre   £

Factory: single storey owners requirements	£/m2	300-400
Office buildings: owner occupation	£/m2	800-900

Building cost

Factory 2000 m2 x £300-£400	600,000-800,000
Offices 400 m2 x £800-£900	320,000-360,000
Total building cost range	£920,000 to £1,040,000

£

Site clearance	10,000 m2 @ £0.10	1,000
Demolition brick building	5,000 m3 @ £4.00	20,000
Earth moving to level site	1,000 m3 @ £2.50	2,500
Hydraulic mulch seeding	2,000 m2 @ £4,000/ha	800
Planting transplants	500 nr @ £3.50	1,750
Planting shrubs	1,000 nr @ £7.00	7,000
Fences chain link 1.4m high	400 m @ £15.00	6,000
Gates	1 set @ £450	450
Tarmac road 7.5m	150 m @ £190	28,500
Car park spaces	100 nr @ £500	50,000
		£ 118,000

Drainage to main outlet	150m of 225mm Hepseal @ £40	6,000
	3 nr manholes @ £800	2,400
Car parking drainage	300m of 150mm Hepseal @ £25	7,500
	5 nr manholes @ £800	4,000
	Sundry drainage	500
Incoming services	Allowance for L.A. charges	2,000

	£ 140,400
Design contingencies 10% say	14,040
	£ 154,440

Total estimated cost of scheme   £

Factory: Average of £600,000 and £800,000	700,000
Offices: Average of £320,000 and £360,000	340,000
Carried forward	£ 1,040,000

Brought forward	£ 1,040,000
Siteworks	154,440
Total budget estimate	£ 1,194,440
Allowances for regional factor x 0.97	1,158,607
Allowance for fees (chapter 14) @ 13%	155,277
	£ 1,313,884
Including contingencies say	£ 1,400,000

Example 2

Client requirements

1. Office: city centre 5000m2 office accommodation plus car park
2. Site: 1100m2
3. Location: London
4. Site work: existing premises demolished by vendor, adjacent
               property on one side to be underpinned by developer.

From Chapter 1 - Building prices per square metre.

	£
Offices for owner occupation good standard	800-900
Extra for 4-7 floors.	150-200

Assumed offices can be provided in six floors with basement car park
and services on seventh floor.

	£
5000m2 @ £900 offices	4,500,000
1000m2 @ £500 car park	500,000
850m2 @ £750 service floor	637,500
Extra for 4 - 7 floors 6850m2 @ £175	1,198,750
	£ 6,836,250
Allowance for underpinning 35m @ £700	24,500
	£ 6,860,750
Extra for difficultes due to confined site	150,000
Total budget estimate	£ 7,010,750

Total budget estimate		£ 7,010,750
Allowance for regional factor x 1.09		630,967
Allowance for fees (chapter 14) @ 13%		<u>911,398</u>
	£	<u>8,553,115</u>
Including contingencies say	£	<u>8,650,000</u>

The Regional Factors Map overleaf is prepared by the Building Cost Information Service of the Royal Institute of Chartered Surveyors and is taken from a larger study of county factors published in the BCIS Quarterly Review of Building Prices available from BCIS, 85/87, Clarence Street, Kingston upon Thames, Surrey, KT1 1RB.

It should be remembered that these indices should only be applied to overall project costs and not to individual rates.

Figure 1 Standard Statistical Region showing Regional Factors based on
national average = 1.00

Part One

Building Work

1   **Building prices per square metre**
2   **Elemental costs**
3   **Composite rates**

The following range of costs can be applied to the types of projects listed. They include an allowance for preliminary and general items but exclude external works, fittings furniture and professional fees. LP and H stands for lighting, power and heating.

Because of the wide variation in design and standards required even in buildings with the same end-use, the figures are generally stated in a range and should only be used as a rough guide to construction costs.

Cost per square metre

Factories

£

Simple single storey steel frame (excluding LP and H)	225-250
Single storey for letting (including LP and H)	275-300
Single storey, owner's requirements	300-400
Single storey, heavy industrial use	425-600
Single storey, complex special requirements	550-800
Two storey, steel frame, owner's requirements	700-850
Two storey, technology with offices	800-1150
Two storey, with air conditioned environment	1400-1950

Warehouses		Cost per square metre £
Low rise (7m), drive in (excluding LP and H)		220-275
Medium rise (14m), loading bays, owners requirements		350-425
High rise (15-20m), loading bays, owners requirements		400-550
Air conditioned, cold rooms	Add	175-350

Office buildings

Offices for letting, minimum standard	500-700
Extra for 4-7 floors	150-200
Extra for air conditioning	150-200
Offices for owner occupation, good standard	800-900
Extra for 4-7 floors	150-200
Extra for air conditioning	200-300
Offices for owner occupation, high standard	1200-1800
Extra for over 10 floors	250-500
Office attached to factory buildings	475-600
Refurbishment of existing office buildings	300-550
Refurbishment of existing office buildings	300-550
Extra for air conditioning	200-300
Extra for prestige building	400-600

Commercial premises

Supermarket buildings	
Shell only	300-400
Complete	1000-1200

	Cost per square metre £
Retail warehouse outlets for letting	250-350
Extra for fitting out	200-250
Shopping parades (flats over) for letting	450-550

Public service buildings

Ambulance stations	500-700
Banks	
small local branch	750-950
city head office	950-1400
Building societies	
small local branch	700-900
city head office	900-1300
Courts	
magistrates	750-950
county	850-1100
Police stations	550-850
Prisons	950-1100

Leisure premises

Cinemas	
shell only	375-475
complete (including equipment)	700-900
Clubhouses	
generally	450-650
golf	675-950
Community centres	550-750
Halls	
village	550-700
concert	1300-2000
Ice rinks	700-800

Leisure premises (cont'd)	Cost per square metre £
Public houses	700-1000
Restaurants	800-1000
Sport halls	500-650
Swimming pools	
school	600-800
local	750-900
international	900-1050
leisure/fun	950-1200

Educational premises

Libraries	
local	600-750
city	750-950
Museums	
local	650-950
city	850-1250
Schools	
nursery	600-950
primary	550-800
middle	600-700
sixth form colleges	600-800
special	500-750
Universities	600-900

Health and welfare

Doctors' clinics	500-700
Health centres	800-1200
Hospitals	
general	700-900
private	800-1000
Nursing homes	
childrens	550-700
old peoples	700-1000

	Cost per square metre £
Housing	
Local authority and housing association	
bungalows, terraced	400-480
bungalows, semi-detached	450-525
houses, terraced	350-440
houses, semi-detached	400-475
flats, low rise	410-475
sheltered	450-550
Private	
bungalows, semi-detached	500-600
bungalows, detached	550-650
houses, semi-detached	450-650
houses, detached	500-700
flats, low rise, standard	480-600
flats, low rise, luxury	650-850
Hotels	
Motels	650-750
Town - medium quality	700-1100
City centre - luxury quality	1400-2000
Transport facilities	
Airport hangars	900-1150
Airport passenger terminal buildings	1200-1500
Bus stations	500-700
Car parking	
Multi level	250-350
Underground	350-500
Garages and showrooms	
Car showrooms	450-700
Petrol service stations	700-1000

Elemental costs

The following analyses are intended to give the reader a broad selection of the cost of different types of buildings showing the varying costs of the elements. They should be used with care when constructing a cost plan because various methods of construction can affect the costs per square metre considerably.

However, it is obviously more accurate to build up the elemental costs than to apply a single all-in rate for the whole building. External works, where shown, will also affect the final cost per square metre more than many of the other elements and consideration of this item is particularly important. Some of the figures may be distorted due to rounding off. The following buildings are included:

Factory unit - for letting
          - owner requirements

Warehouse unit, low rise, drive in

Offices   - for letting, two floors
          - owner occupied

Superstore - shell only
          - complete

Public house

Health centre

Nursing home for elderly - one storey

Housing - housing association, low rise flats

Garage, workshop and showroom

School - middle

Bank - two storey

Magistrates court - three storey

Ambulance station

Hotel - two storey

Students' hostel

FACTORY: SINGLE STOREY FOR LETTING

Gross floor area 15,200m Element No.	Cost/m2 floor area £	% of cost	Total cost of element £
1 Substructure	43.47	15.37	660,776
2 Frame	35.04	12.37	532,577
3 Upper floors	3.23	1.14	49,089
4 Roof	22.42	7.93	340,827
5 Staircases	4.12	1.46	62,661
6 External walls	19.47	6.89	295,980
7 Windows and external doors	10.83	3.83	164,598
8 Partitions and internal walls	10.29	3.64	156,453
9 Internal doors	5.12	1.81	77,878
10 Wall finishes	0.27	0.10	4,102
11 Floor finishes	9.06	3.20	137,666
12 Ceiling finishes	2.01	0.71	30,477
13 Fittings	0.06	0.02	857
14 Sanitary fittings	4.49	1.59	68,272
15 Waste soil and overflow pipes	1.75	0.62	26,517
16 Hot and cold water services	1.68	0.59	25,516
17 Heating installation	27.62	9.77	419,839
18 Ventilation installation	10.92	3.86	165,982
19 Gas services	-	-	-
Carried forward £	211.85	74.92	3,220,067

Element No.	Cost/m2 floor area £	% of cost	Total cost of element £
Brought forward	211.85	74.92	3,220,067
20 Electrical installation	16.97	6.00	257,900
21 Lift installation	-	-	-
22 Special services installation	3.42	1.22	52,040
23 Builders work in connection with services	2.47	0.87	37,497
24 Drainage) 25 External works)	48.05	16.99	730.343
TOTAL £	282.76	100.00	4,297,847

FACTORY: SINGLE STOREY, OWNER'S REQUIREMENTS

Gross floor area: 1720m2

Element No.	Cost/m2 floor area £	% of cost	Total cost of element £
1 Substructure	60.44	16.31	103,954
2 Frame	33.26	8.98	57,206
3 Upper floors	-	-	-
4 Roof	72.46	19.56	124,633
5 Staircases	-	-	-
6 External walls	26.02	7.02	44,760
Carried forward £	192.18	51.87	330,553

FACTORY: SINGLE STOREY, OWNER'S REQUIREMENTS (cont'd)

Element No.	Cost/m2 floor area £	% of cost	Total cost of element £
Brought forward	192.18	51.87	330,553
7 Windows and external doors	17.61	4.75	30,225
8 Partitions and internal walls	8.65	2.34	14,883
9 Internal doors	1.89	0.51	3,252
10 Wall finishes	9.79	2.64	16,841
11 Floor finishes	4.29	1.16	7,383
12 Ceiling finishes	3.46	0.94	5,963
13 Fittings	1.11	0.30	1,915
14 Sanitary fittings	4.78	1.29	8,225
15 Waste soil and overflow pipes	1.61	0.43	2,770
16 Hot and cold water services	3.61	0.98	6,228
17 Heating installation	1.09	0.29	1,870
18 Ventilation installation	3.79	1.02	6,524
19 Gas services	-	-	-
20 Electrical installation	13.39	3.62	23,041
21 Lift installation	-	-	-
22 Special services installation	-	-	-
23 Builders work in connection with services	-	-	-
Carried forward £	267.25	72.14	459,673

Element No.	Cost/m2 floor area £	% of cost	Total cost of element £
Brought forward	267.25	72.14	459,673
24 Drainage	21.86	5.90	37,612
25 External works	81.38	21.96	139,970
TOTAL	£ 370.49	100.00	637,255

WAREHOUSE: LOW RISE DRIVE IN (EXCLUDING LIGHT, HEAT OR POWER)

Gross floor area: 11,150m2 Element No.	Cost/m2 floor area £	% of cost	Total cost of element £
1 Substructure	50.30	19.47	560,780
2 Frame	64.54	24.99	719,688
3 Upper floors	-	-	-
4 Roof	52.15	20.19	581,477
5 Staircases	-	-	-
6 External walls)			
7 Windows and external doors)	55.15	21.35	614,953
8 Partitions and internal walls)			
9 Internal doors)	4.08	1.58	45,527
10 Wall finishes	0.77	0.30	8,587
11 Floor finishes	0.69	0.26	7,606
12 Ceiling finishes	1.62	0.63	18,086
13 Fittings	0.12	0.05	1,316
Carried forward	£ 229.42	88.82	2,558,020

WAREHOUSE: LOW RISE, DRIVE IN (EXCLUDING LIGHT, HEAT OR POWER) (cont'd)

Element No.	Cost/m2 floor area £	% of cost	Total cost of element £
Brought forward	229.42	88.82	2,558,020
14 Sanitary fittings	-	-	-
15 Waste soil and overflow pipes	0.51	0.20	5,663
16 Hot and cold water services	-	-	-
17 Heating installation	2.74	1.06	30,570
18 Ventilation installation	-	-	-
19 Gas services	2.00	0.77	22,273
20 Electrical installation	-	-	-
21 Lift installation	-	-	-
22 Special services installation	-	-	-
23 Builders work in connection with services	-	-	-
24 Drainage	23.65	9.15	263,694
25 External works (not included)	-	-	-
TOTAL £	258.32	100.00	2,880,520

OFFICES: FOR LETTING MINIMUM STANDARD, TWO FLOORS

Gross floor area: 1,500m2

Element No.	Cost/m2 floor area £	% of cost	Total cost of element £
1 Substructure	82.88	12.58	124,316
2 Frame	31.81	4.83	47,711
3 Upper floors	39.67	6.02	59,344
4 Roof	43.51	6.61	65,263
5 Staircases	-	-	-
6 External walls	63.37	9.62	95,423
7 Windows and external doors	138.46	21.03	207,696
8 Partitions and internal walls	4.96	0.75	7,436
9 Internal doors	11.18	1.70	16,775
10 Wall finishes	18.61	2.83	27,909
11 Floor finishes	25.47	3.87	38,192
12 Ceiling finishes	15.76	2.39	23,640
13 Fittings	0.45	0.07	672
14 Sanitary fittings	3.89	0.59	5,844
15 Waste soil and overflow pipes	5.25	0.80	7,872
16 Hot and cold water services	-	-	-
17 Heating installation	38.06	5.78	57,076
18 Ventilation installation	-	-	-
19 Gas services	-	-	-
Carried forward	£ 523.33	79.47	785,169

OFFICES: FOR LETTING MINIMUM STANDARD, TWO FLOORS (cont'd)

Element No.	Cost/m2 floor area £	% of cost	Total cost of element £
Brought forward	523.33	79.47	785,169
20 Electrical installation	39.72	6.03	59,585
21 Lift installation	-	-	-
22 Special services installation	1.18	0.18	1,766
23 Builders work in connection with services	1.65	0.25	2,474
24 Drainage	8.15	1.24	12,218
25 External works	84.52	12.83	126,769
TOTAL £	658.55	100.00	987,981

OFFICES: FOR OWNER OCCUPATION, GOOD STANDARD

Gross floor area 4215m2 Element No.	Cost/m2 floor area £	% of cost	Total cost of element £
1 Substructure	89.32	10.46	376,566
2 Frame)			
3 Upper floors)	104.52	12.24	440,850
4 Roof	10.98	1.29	46,274
5 Staircases in frame			
6 External walls	89.21	10.41	376,086
7 Windows and external doors	63.78	7.47	268,892
Carried forward £	357.81	41.87	1,508,668

Element No.		Cost/m2 floor area £	% of cost	Total cost of element £
Brought forward	£	357.81	41.87	1,508,668
8 Partitions and internal wall		25.08	2.93	105,719
9 Internal doors		24.13	2.83	101,722
10 Wall finishes		43.48	5.09	183,307
11 Floor finishes		44.30	5.18	186,754
12 Ceiling finishes		42.82	5.02	180,533
13 Fittings		42.76	5.12	184,496
14 Sanitary fittings		5.14	0.60	21,662
15 Waste soil and overflow pipes)				
16 Hot and cold water services)				
17 Heating installation)		114.85	13.44	484,196
18 Ventilation installation)				
19 Gas services)				
20 Electrical installation		53.88	6.31	227,199
21 Lift installation		32.25	3.78	135,948
22 Special services installation		6.63	0.78	27,933
23 Builders work in connection with services		10.80	1.26	45,502
24 Drainage		9.72	1.14	41,014
25 External works		39.76	4.65	167,613
TOTAL	£	853.41	100.00	3,602,266

SUPERMARKET: SHELL ONLY

Gross floor area 2,625m2 Element No.	Cost/m2 floor area £	% of cost	Total cost of element £
1 Substructure	63.58	19.11	168,995
2 Frame	82.40	24.77	219,019
3 Upper floors	3.47	1.04	9,223
4 Roof	75.87	22.81	201,662
5 Staircases	1.24	0.37	3,295
6 External walls	32.46	9.76	86,278
7 Windows and external doors	26.42	7.94	70,224
8 Partitions and internal walls	-	-	-
9 Internal doors	-	-	-
10 Wall finishes	2.14	0.64	5,688
11 Floor finishes	1.78	0.54	4,731
12 Ceiling finishes	3.19	0.96	8,479
13 Fittings	-	-	-
14 Sanitary fittings	-	-	-
15 Waste soil and overflow pipes	1.76	0.53	4,678
16 Hot and cold water services	2.14	0.64	5,688
17 Heating installation	-	-	-
18 Ventilation installation	-	-	-
19 Gas services	-	-	-
Carried forward £	296.45	89.11	787,960

Element No.		Cost/m2 floor area £	% of cost	Total cost of element £
Brought forward	£	296.45	89.11	787,960
20 Electrical installation		-	-	-
21 Lift installation		-	-	-
22 Special services installation		-	-	-
23 Builders work in connection with services		-	-	-
24 Drainage		14.60	4.39	38,806
25 External works (nominal)		21.62	6.50	57,465
TOTAL	£	332.67	100.00	884,231

SUPERMARKET: COMPLETE

Gross floor area 2657m2 Element No.		Cost/m2 floor area £	% of cost	Total cost of element £
1 Substructure		63.58	5.60	168,995
2 Frame		82.40	7.27	219,019
3 Upper floors		3.47	0.31	9,223
4 Roof		75.87	6.69	201,662
5 Staircases		1.24	0.11	3,295
6 External walls		32.46	2.86	86,278
7 Windows and external doors		26.42	2.33	70,224
8 Partitions and internal walls		17.87	1.58	47,498
Carried forward	£	303.31	26.75	806,194

SUPERMARKET: COMPLETE (cont'd)

Element No.		Cost/m2 floor area £	% of cost	Total cost of element £
Brought forward	£	303.31	26.75	806,194
9 Internal doors		8.21	0.72	21,822
10 Wall finishes		15.97	1.41	42,448
11 Floor finishes		27.26	2.40	72,457
12 Ceiling finishes		21.48	1.89	57,093
13 Fittings		97.80	8.62	259,952
14 Sanitary fittings		5.78	0.51	15,363
15 Waste soil and overflow pipes		6.24	0.55	16,585
16 Hot and cold water services		14.22	1.25	37,796
17 Heating installation)				
)		98.42	8.68	261,600
18 Ventilation installation)				
19 Gas services		4.29	0.38	11,402
20 Electrical installation		103.88	9.16	276,113
21 Lift installation		-	-	-
22 Special services installation		287.58	25.38	764,387
23 Builders work in connection with services		17.43	1.54	46,488
24 Drainage		18.43	1.63	48,986
25 External works		103.49	9.13	275,076
TOTAL	£	1,133.79	100.00	3,013,762

PUBLIC HOUSE

Gross floor area 630m2 Element No.	Cost/m2 floor area £	% of cost	Total cost of element £
1 Substructure	130.87	13.40	82,452
2 Frame	9.02	0.92	5,683
3 Upper floors	7.70	0.79	4,856
4 Roof	88.21	9.04	55,577
5 Staircases (in upper floors)	-	-	-
6 External walls	47.88	4.91	30,164
7 Windows and external doors	28.20	2.89	17,766
8 Partitions and internal walls	20.81	2.13	13,106
9 Internal doors	26.46	2.71	16,669
10 Wall finishes	37.66	3.86	23,726
11 Floor finishes	41.29	4.23	26,011
12 Ceiling finishes	30.10	3.08	18,960
13 Fittings	94.22	9.65	59,362
14 Sanitary fittings	16.15	1.66	10,178
15 Waste soil and overflow pipes) 16 Hot and cold water services) 17 Heating installation) 18 Ventilation installation)	80.32	8.23	50,596
19 Gas services	-	-	-
20 Electrical installation	63.92	6.55	40,273
Carried forward	£ 722.81	74.05	455,379

PUBLIC HOUSE (cont'd)

Element No.		Cost/m2 floor area £	% of cost	Total cost of element £
Brought forward	£	722.81	74.05	455,379
21 Lift installation		-	-	-
22 Special services installation		27.53	2.82	17,341
23 Builders work in connection with services		-	-	-
24 Drainage		45.94	4.71	28,940
25 External works		179.80	18.42	113,280
TOTAL	£	976.08	100.00	614,940

HEALTH CENTRE

Gross floor area 1400m2 Element No.	Cost/m2 floor area £	% of cost	Total cost of element £
1 Substructure	91.66	9.90	128,318
2 Frame	-	-	-
3 Upper floors	13.27	1.43	18,576
4 Roof	65.46	7.06	91,467
5 Staircases	7.33	0.79	10,265
6 External walls	55.25	5.97	77,351
7 Windows and external doors	58.85	6.36	82,395
8 Partitions and internal walls	28.39	3.07	39,745
9 Internal doors	48.91	5.28	68,478
Carried forward £	369.12	39.86	516,595

Element No.	Cost/m2 floor area £	% of cost	Total cost of element £
Brought forward	£ 369.12	39.86	516,595
10 Wall finishes	32.41	3.50	45,378
11 Floor finishes	32.75	3.54	45,848
12 Ceiling finishes	14.54	1.57	20,440
13 Fittings	71.49	7.74	100,354
14 Sanitary fittings	18.26	2.00	25,910
15 Waste soil and overflow pipes	1.94	0.21	2,709
16 Hot and cold water services	43.26	4.67	60,566
17 Heating installation	112.01	12.10	156,812
18 Ventilation installation	17.63	1.91	24,684
19 Gas services	0.36	0.04	539
20 Electrical installation	102.55	11.08	143,569
21 Lift installation	15.06	1.63	21,076
22 Special services installation	67.71	7.32	94.782
23 Builders work in connection with services	26.25	2.83	36,683
24 Drainage (not included)	-	-	-
25 External works (not included)	-	-	-
TOTAL	£ 925.34	100.00	1,295,945

NURSING HOME FOR OLD PEOPLE: ONE STOREY

Gross floor area 1300m2 Element No.	Cost/m2 floor area £	% of cost	Total cost of element £
1 Substructure	68.44	7.42	88,978
2 Frame	-	-	-
3 Upper floors	-	-	-
4 Roof	117.54	12.74	152,908
5 Staircases	-	-	-
6 External walls	44.08	4.78	57,292
7 Windows and external doors	55.05	5.96	71,544
8 Partitions and internal walls	21.16	2.29	27,514
9 Internal doors	44.95	4.87	58,435
10 Wall finishes	29.73	3.22	38,655
11 Floor finishes	35.63	3.86	46,322
12 Ceiling finishes	13.02	1.41	16,930
13 Fittings	70.94	7.69	92,218
14 Sanitary fittings	9.13	0.99	11,874
15 Waste soil and overflow pipes	0.86	0.09	1,122
16 Hot and cold water services	38.37	4.16	49,878
17 Heating installation	42.31	4.59	55,000
18 Ventilation installation	9.30	1.01	12,079
19 Gas services	1.58	0.17	2,053
Carried forward	£ 602.09	65.25	791,797

Element No.		Cost/m2 floor area £	% of cost	Total cost of element £
Brought forward	£	602.09	65.25	791,797
20 Electrical installation		60.41	6.93	83,731
21 Lift installation		-	-	-
22 Special services installation		38.51	4.17	50,065
23 Builders work in connection with services		38.07	4.13	49,495
24 Drainage		37.26	4.04	48,429
25 External works		142.40	15.48	185,285
TOTAL	£	918.74	100.00	1,208,802

HOUSING: HOUSING ASSOCIATION LOW RISE FLATS

Gross floor area 1280m2 Element No.		Cost/m2 floor area £	% of cost	Total cost of element £
1 Substructure		44.46	9.45	57,164
2 Frame		-	-	-
3 Upper floors		14.84	3.10	18,741
4 Roof		51.20	10.83	65,528
5 Staircases		6.53	1.38	8,356
6 External walls		54.42	11.51	69,652
7 Windows and external doors		47.31	10.01	60,566
8 Partitions and internal walls		49.76	10.53	63,692
9 Internal doors		37.29	7.88	47,728
Carried forward	£	305.81	64.69	391,427

HOUSING: HOUSING ASSOCIATION LOW RISE FLATS

Element No.		Cost/m2 floor area £	% of cost	Total cost of element £
Brought forward	£	305.81	64.69	391,427
10 Wall finishes		22.00	4.65	28,161
11 Floor finishes		13.19	2.79	16,882
12 Ceiling finishes		32.21	6.81	41,218
13 Fittings		12.94	2.80	16,929
14 Sanitary fittings)) 15 Waste soil and overflow pipes)) 16 Hot and cold water services)		20.49	4.33	26,227
17 Heating installation)) 18 Ventilation installation)		40.60	8.59	51,971
19 Gas services		-	-	-
20 Electrical installation		25.17	5.34	32,220
21 Lift installation		-	-	-
22 Special services installation		-	-	-
23 Builders work in connection with services		-	-	-
24 Drainage (not included)		-	-	-
25 External works (not included)		-	-	-
TOTAL	£	472.41	100.00	605,035

GARAGE: WORKSHOPS AND SHOWROOM (EXCLUDING FORECOURT)

Gross floor area 870m2 Element No.	Cost/m2 floor area £	% of cost	Total cost of element £
1 Substructure	75.08	10.14	65,271
2 Frame	116.19	15.70	101,092
3 Upper floors	3.11	0.42	2,705
4 Roof (included in frame)	-	-	-
5 Staircases	-	-	-
6 External walls	35.36	4.78	30,765
7 Windows and external doors	70.41	9.52	61,253
8 Partitions and internal walls	41.24	5.87	35,882
9 Internal doors	11.15	1.51	9,699
10 Wall finishes	28.13	3.80	24,468
11 Floor finishes	59.25	8.01	51,544
12 Ceiling finishes	6.28	0.85	5,469
13 Fittings	4.92	0.67	4,281
14 Sanitary fittings	-	-	-
15 Waste soil and overflow pipes	-	-	-
16 Hot and cold water services	52.81	7.14	45,955
17 Heating installation	-	-	-
18 Ventilation installation	-	-	-
19 Gas services	-	-	-
Carried forward	£ 503.93	68.41	438,384

GARAGE: WORKSHOPS AND SHOWROOM (EXCLUDING FORECOURT) (cont'd)

Element No.		Cost/m2 floor area £	% of cost	Total cost of element £
Brought forward	£	503.93	68.41	438,384
20 Electrical installation		53.55	7.24	46,584
21 Lift installation		-	-	-
22 Special services installation		-	-	-
23 Builders work in connection with services		-	-	-
24 Drainage		55.42	7.19	48,218
25 External works		126.98	17.16	110,471
TOTAL	£	739.88	100.00	643,657

MIDDLE SCHOOL

Gross floor area 2000m2 Element No.		Cost/m2 floor area £	% of cost	Total cost of element £
1 Substructure		64.04	9.88	128,071
2 Frame		49.85	7.69	99,685
3 Upper floors		18.97	2.93	37,929
4 Roof		23.55	3.63	47,082
5 Staircases		11.77	1.82	23,549
6 External walls		50.52	7.79	101,035
7 Windows and external doors		30.90	4.77	61,808
Carried forward	£	249.60	38.51	499,159

Element No.		Cost/m2 floor area £	% of cost	Total cost of element £
Brought forward	£	249.60	38.51	499,159
8 Partitions and internal walls		23.22	3.58	46,441
9 Internal doors		19.48	3.01	38,959
10 Wall finishes		11.43	1.75	22,679
11 Floor finishes		23.30	3.60	46,599
12 Ceiling finishes		10.52	1.76	22,831
13 Fittings		21.48	3.32	42,967
14 Sanitary fittings		61.95	0.96	12,386
15 Waste soil and overflow pipes		10.59	1.63	21,172
16 Hot and cold water services		14.41	2.22	28,820
17 Heating installation		30.16	5.12	66,313
18 Ventilation installation		8.49	1.31	16,963
19 Gas services		4.68	0.72	9,360
20 Electrical installation		31.70	4.89	63,409
21 Lift installation		22.68	3.50	45,355
22 Special services installation		0.58	0.09	1,150
23 Builders work in connection with services		11.21	1.73	22,423
24 Drainage		16.63	2.57	33,263
25 External works		128.03	19.73	256,071
TOTAL	£	700.14	100.00	1,296,320

BANK: TWO STOREY, STEEL FRAMED

Gross floor area 830m2 Element No.	Cost/m2 floor area £	% of cost	Total cost of element £
1 Substructure	56.93	5.08	47,252
2 Frame	191.74	17.11	159,147
3 Upper floors	65.94	5.88	54,726
4 Roof	72.22	6.44	59,943
5 Staircases	28.34	2.53	23,525
6 External walls	246.09	22.00	204,256
7 Windows and external doors	65.16	5.81	54,082
8 Partitions and internal walls	28.35	2.53	23,528
9 Internal doors	12.80	1.14	10,628
10 Wall finishes	8.62	0.77	7,152
11 Floor finishes	41.36	3.69	34,327
12 Ceiling finishes	25.64	2.29	21,280
13 Fittings	42.04	3.75	34,893
14 Sanitary fittings	3.58	0.32	2,969
15 Waste soil and overflow pipes	2.43	0.22	2,021
16 Hot and cold water services) 17 Heating installation)	97.69	8.72	81,090
18 Ventilation installation	-	-	-
19 Gas services	-	-	-
20 Electrical installation	47.93	4.28	39,780
Carried forward	£ 1,036.86	92.56	860,599

Element No.	Cost/m2 floor area £	% of cost	Total cost of element £
Brought forward	£ 1,036.86	92.56	860,599
21 Lift installation	-	-	-
22 Special services installation	46.22	4.06	38,364
23 Builders work in connection with services	2.69	0.24	2,235
24 Drainage	9.12	0.81	7,572
25 External works	26.07	2.33	21,635
TOTAL	£ 1120.96	100.00	930,405

MAGISTRATES COURT: THREE STOREY, STEEL FRAMED

Gross floor area 2400m2 Element No.	Cost/m2 floor area £	% of cost	Total cost of element £
1 Substructure	62.60	6.82	150,232
2 Frame	193.07	21.02	463,362
3 Upper floors	34.18	3.72	82,029
4 Roof (in 2)	-	-	-
5 Staircases	15.24	1.66	36,584
6 External walls	39.12	4.26	93,880
7 Windows and external doors	39.69	4.32	95,248
8 Partitions and internal walls	36.58	3.98	87,791
9 Internal doors	34.74	3.78	83,384
10 Wall finishes	52.26	5.69	125,416
Carried forward	£ 507.48	55.25	1,217,926

MAGISTRATES COURT (cont'd)

Element No.		Cost/m2 floor area £	% of cost	Total cost of element £
Brought forward	£	507.48	55.25	1,217,926
11 Floor finishes		43.01	4.68	103,212
12 Ceiling finishes		21.89	2.38	52,539
13 Fittings		52.49	5.72	125,985
14 Sanitary fittings		9.64	1.05	23,126
15 Waste soil and overflow pipes)				
16 Hot and cold water services)		124.99	13.61	299,982
17 Heating installation)				
18 Ventilation installation		-	-	-
19 Gas services		-	-	-
20 Electrical installation		78.03	8.50	187,275
21 Lift installation		15.53	1.69	37,275
22 Special services installation		-	-	-
23 Builders work in connection with services		-	-	-
24 Drainage)				
25 External works)		65.26	7.12	156,612
TOTAL	£	918.32	100.00	2,203,932

AMBULANCE STATION: SINGLE STOREY WITH OFFICE AND MESS ROOM

Gross floor area 300m2 Element No.	Cost/m2 floor area £	% of cost	Total cost of element £
1 Substructure	86.75	12.05	26,026
2 Frame	131.36	18.24	39,408
3 Upper floors	-	-	-
4 Roof (in 2)	-	-	-
5 Staircases	-	-	-
6 External walls	51.27	7.12	15,382
7 Windows and external doors	87.86	12.20	26,358
8 Partitions and internal walls	40.11	5.57	12,034
9 Internal doors	9.36	1.30	2,808
10 Wall finishes	12.82	1.78	3,845
11 Floor finishes	19.59	2.72	5,877
12 Ceiling finishes	4.08	0.57	1,224
13 Fittings	13.12	1.85	3,937
14 Sanitary fittings)			
15 Waste soil and overflow pipes)	94.92	13.18	28,475
16 Hot and cold water services)			
17 Heating installation)			
18 Ventilation installation	-	-	-
19 Gas services	-	-	-
Carried forward	£ 551.24	76.58	165,374

AMBULANCE STATION (cont'd)

Element No.		Cost/m2 floor area £	% of cost	Total cost of element £
Brought forward	£	551.24	76.58	165,374
20 Electrical installation		4.51	6.27	13,546
21 Lift installation		-	-	-
22 Special services installation		-	-	-
23 Builders work in connection with services		-	-	-
24 Drainage		-	-	-
25 External works		123.51	17.15	37,053
TOTAL	£	679.26	100.00	215,973

HOTEL: TWO STOREY WITH LEISURE FACILITIES

Gross floor area 3200m2 Element No.		Cost/m2 floor area £	% of cost	Total cost of element £
1 Substructure		29.35	4.11	93,904
2 Frame		71.98	10.10	230,355
3 Upper floors		10.48	1.47	33,527
4 Roof (in 2)		-	-	-
5 Staircases (in 2)		-	-	-
6 External walls		85.67	12.02	274,144
Carried forward	£	197.48	27.70	631,930

	Cost/m2 floor area £	% of cost	Total cost of element £
Brought forward £	197.48	27.70	631,930
7 Windows and external doors	20.03	2.81	64,089
8 Partitions and internal walls	19.32	2.71	61,808
9 Internal doors	14.54	2.04	46,527
10 Wall finishes	29.79	4.18	95,335
11 Floor finishes	28.51	4.00	91,229
12 Ceiling finishes	26.16	3.67	83,703
13 Fittings	56.38	7.91	180,406
14 Sanitary fittings)			
15 Waste soil and overflow pipes)			
16 Hot and cold water services)	169.42	23.77	542,133
17 Heating installation)			
18 Ventilation installation)			
19 Gas services)			
20 Electrical installation	65.14	9.14	208,460
21 Lift installation	22.09	3.10	70,703
22 Special services installation	-	-	-
23 Builders work in connection with services	-	-	-
24 Drainage)	67.02	8.97	214,458
25 External works)			
TOTAL £	715.88	100.00	2,290,781

STUDENTS' HOSTEL

Gross floor area 2,400m2 Element No.	Cost/m2 floor area £	% of cost	Total cost of element £
1 Substructure	37.35	5.57	89,642
2 Frame (in 6)	-	-	-
3 Upper floors	24.13	3.60	57,921
4 Roof	21.77	3.25	52,248
5 Staircases	13.35	1.99	32,037
6 External walls	62.19	9.28	149,248
7 Windows and external doors	71.71	10.71	172,112
8 Partitions and internal walls	40.51	6.04	97,212
9 Internal doors	42.49	6.34	101,979
10 Wall finishes	33.86	5.05	81,265
11 Floor finishes	28.84	4.31	69,221
12 Ceiling finishes	13.83	2.07	33,200
13 Fittings	24.84	3.71	59,612
14 Sanitary fittings	25.88	3.86	62,117
15 Waste soil and overflow pipes	11.34	1.69	27,220
16 Hot and cold water services	38.27	5.71	91,841
17 Heating installation	75.01	11.24	180,022
18 Ventilation installation	-	-	-
19 Gas services	-	-	-
20 Electrical installation	81.76	12.21	198,212
Carried forward	£ 647.13	96.63	1,555,109

Element No.		1300m2 floor area £	Cost/m2 cost	% of	Total cost of element £
Brought forward	£	647.13	96.63		1,555,109
21 Lift installation		-	-		-
22 Special services installation		-	-		-
23 Builders work in connection with services		-	-		-
24 Drainage		22.59	3.37		54,220
25 External works (not included)		-	-		-
TOTAL	£	669.72	100.00		1,609,329

When there is time to prepare approximate quantities to assess the budget value of a project, the following rates will be useful. They have been compiled by combining various items to produce composite rates.

SUBSTRUCTURES	Unit	£
Excavate, dispose, uphold and prepare formation in basements	m3	12
Extra for excavating in		
made ground	m3	8-12
rock	m3	20-25
concrete or brickwork	m3	15-20
reinforced concrete	m3	25-30
Concrete (11.5N/mm2 40mm aggregate) in bases below formation including excavation, formwork and reinforcement, size		
600 x 600 x 300mm	nr	15-18
750 x 750 x 500mm	nr	25-32
1000 x 1000 x 750mm	nr	65-80
1200 x 1200 x 1000mm	nr	120-140
Concrete (21N/mm2 20mm aggregate) in basement floor slab including blinding, Visqueen and reinforcement at 100 kg per m3, thickness		
250mm	m2	35-40
300mm	m2	40-45

Substructures (cont'd)	Unit	£
500mm	m2	55-80

Concrete (21N/mm2 20mm aggregate) in basement walls including formwork and reinforcement at 115 kg per m3, thickness

250mm	m2	85-90
300mm	m2	95-100
500mm	m2	120-130

Concrete (21N/mm2 20mm aggregate) in ground beams including excavation, formwork and reinforcement size

500 x 500	m	55-65
750 x 500	m	75-80
900 x 600	m	105-115
1000 x 1000	m	160-190

Concrete (21N/mm2 50mm aggregate) in ground beams including excavation, formwork and reinforcement size

500 x 500	m	65-75

Strip foundations for trench width 600mm including excavation disposal, earthwork support, concrete foundation (11.5 N/m2, 40mm aggregate) 225mm thick, common brick wall (£125 per thousand) height 600mm, damp proof course

215mm thick	m	45-50
265mm thick cavity wall	m	50-55

	Unit	£

Strip foundations for trench width 600mm including excavation disposal, earthwork support, concrete foundation (11.5 N/m2, 40mm aggregate) 225mm thick, common brick wall (£125 per thousand) height 900 mm, damp proof course

215mm thick	m	60-65
265mm thick cavity wall	m	65-70

Strip foundations for trench width 675mm including excavation disposal, earthwork support, concrete foundation (11.5 N/m2, 40mm aggregate) 225 mm thick, common brick wall (£125 per thousand) height 600mm, damp proof course

327mm thick	m	75-80

Strip foundations for trench width 675mm including excavation disposal, earthwork support, concrete foundation (11.5 N/m2, 40mm aggregate) 225mm thick, common brick wall (£125 per thousand) height 900 mm, damp proof course

327mm thick	m	100-105

Strip foundations for trench width 750mm including excavation disposal, earthwork support, concrete foundation (11.5 N/m2, 40 mm aggregate) 300mm thick, common brick wall (£125 per thousand) height 600 mm, damp proof course

450mm thick	m	95-100

Substructures (cont'd)	Unit	£

Strip foundations for trench width 750mm including excavation disposal, earthwork support, concrete foundation (11.5 N/m2, 40mm aggregate) 300mm thick, common brick wall (£125 per thousand) height 900 mm, damp proof course

450mm thick	m	125-130
Underpinning adjoining property	m	600-700

Piling

See Civil Engineering - Chapters 4 and 5.

FRAME AND UPPER FLOORS

Reinforced concrete frame and floors	m2	115-130
Extra for heavy floor loading	m2	25-35
Extra for large spans, normal loading	m2	20-35
Steel frame, concrete encased and floors	m2	135-150
Extra for heavy floor loading	m2	15-25
Extra for large spans, normal loading	m2	25-40

Industrial single storey (ground floor area)

Precast concrete portal frame	m2	50-60
Structural steel portal frame (unencased)	m2	40-50
Structural steel portal frame (columns cased)	m2	55-75
Extra for large spans, normal loading	m2	35-45

	Unit	£
Floors only		
Reinforced concrete suspended slabs	m2	55-70
Precast concrete suspended slabs	m2	30-40
Timber joists and chipboard	m2	20-25
ROOF CONSTRUCTION (no finishes, measured on plan)		
Reinforced concrete roof slabs	m2	40-50
Precast concrete roof slabs	m2	45-55
Softwood flat roofs	m2	35-45
Softwood trussed pitched roofs	m2	15-25
Steel trussed pitched roofs	m2	35-45
Flat roof decking (including finishes)		
Woodwool and three layer felt roofing	m2	40-50
Woodwool and asphalt two coat covering	m2	40-50
Extra for insulation upgrade	m2	5-8
Galvanised steel decking and three layer felt roofing	m2	45-55
Roof coverings (sloping, area measured on plan)		
Concrete interlocking tiles	m2	20-25
Clay pantiles	m2	25-40
Non-asbestos fibre cement slates	m2	30-40
Natural slates (Welsh)	m2	65-75
Plain concrete tiles	m2	30-40
Plain clay tiles	m2	45-55

Roof coverings (cont'd)	Unit	£
Handmade plain clay tiles	m2	55-70
Red cedar shingles	m2	60-65
Verges to pitched roof in softwood and plywood	m	15-20
Eaves to pitched roofs in softwood including PVC gutter	m	20-50
Ridge treatment		
concrete half round tiles	m	12-15
clay half round tiles	m	15-25
Hip treatment		
concrete half round tiles	m	15-18
clay half round tiles	m	20-25
bonnet hip tiles	m	35-45
Roof cladding (sloping, area measured on plan)		
Non-asbestos profiled cladding	m2	15-20
Extra for coloured	m2	2-5
Extra for insulation panels	m2	12-15
Galvanized steel profiled cladding PVF2 coated	m2	20-25
Extra for insulation lining	m2	12-15
Extra for coloured lining	m2	2-5
Aluminium profiled cladding PVF2 coated	m2	25-35
Extra for coloured insulation lining	m2	2-5

	Unit	£
Aluminium profiled cladding with pre-painted finish	m2	30-40

STAIRCASES

Reinforced concrete construction, 3250mm rise, granolithic finish

Straight flight, width

900mm	nr	750-1000
1200mm	nr	1000-1200

Dog-leg flight, width

900mm	nr	1000-1200
1200mm	nr	1200-1500

Reinforced concrete construction, 3250mm rise, terrazzo finish

Straight flight, width

900mm	nr	2000-2400
1200mm	nr	2750-3000

Dog-leg flight, width

900mm	nr	2500-2750
1200mm	nr	3000-3350

Softwood construction, 2600mm rise

straight flight 900mm wide, no balustrade	nr	500-700
two flights with quarter landing, softwood balustrade	nr	700-800
two flights with half landing, hardwood handrail	nr	800-900

Staircases (cont'd)	Unit	£
Mild steel construction, 3000mm rise		
straight flight 900mm wide	nr	2000-2500
two flights with quarter landing	nr	2250-2750
two flights with half landing	nr	2500-3000
Add for additional 300mm rise	nr	200-250
Mild steel spiral construction, 2000mm diameter, 3000mm rise perforated treads, no risers, including balustrade	nr	1500-2500
Extra for heavy duty stair	nr	500-1000
Balustrades, 3250mm rise		
Mild steel		
straight flight	nr	900
dog-leg flight	nr	1200

EXTERNAL WALLS

Common bricks (£125 per thousand) in wall		
102mm thick	m2	30-35
215mm thick	m2	60-65
327mm thick	m2	75-80
440mm thick	m2	95-100
Facing bricks (£300 per thousand) in wall		
102mm thick	m2	55-60
215mm thick in two skins tied together	m2	120-125

	Unit	£
Engineering bricks (£200 per thousand) in wall		
102mm thick	m2	35-40
215mm thick	m2	70-75
327mm thick	m2	95-100
440mm thick	m2	135-140
Lightweight concrete blocks in wall		
75mm thick	m2	18-20
90mm thick	m2	20-22
100mm thick	m2	21-23
140mm thick	m2	28-30
190mm thick	m2	32-35
Dense concrete blocks in wall		
75mm thick	m2	20-22
90mm thick	m2	21-23
100mm thick	m2	23-25
140mm thick	m2	30-32
190mm thick	m2	38-40
215mm thick	m2	43-45
Reconstructed stone blocks in wall		
100mm thick	m2	40-45

External walls (cont'd)	Unit	£
Concrete (21N/mm2, 20mm aggregate) in wall including formwork and reinforcement		
100mm thick	m2	60-65
150mm thick	m2	65-70
200mm thick	m2	70-75
250mm thick	m2	75-80
300mm thick	m2	80-85
Cavity wall formed with one leaf of common brickwork 102 mm thick (£125 per thousand) and one leaf of		
common brickwork (£125 per thousand) 102mm thick	m2	60-70
facing brickwork (£300 per thousand) 102mm thick	m2	85-95
engineering brickwork (£200 per thousand) 102mm thick	m2	65-75
lightweight concrete block 100mm thick	m2	48-55
dense concrete block 100mm thick	m2	53-60
reconstructed stone block 100mm thick	m2	70-80
in situ concrete wall 100mm thick	m2	90-100

Non-load bearing walls (internal finishes excluded)

Precast concrete panels insulated, (with exposed aggregate finish add £50m2)	m2	100-110
Precast concrete with natural stone aggregate facing, (with relief features add £40-60m2)	m2	300-330

	Unit	£
Profiled reinforced cement single skin sheeting on steel sheeting rails	m2	10-15
Extra for insulation and inner lining	m2	10-15
Profiled PVF2 coated galvanized steel sheeting	m2	25-35
Extra for insulation and inner lining	m2	10-15
Extra for full height block internal wall with decoration	m2	20-30
Fully insulated sandwich panels with PVF2 coated galvanized steel sheeting	m2	130-170
Curtain walling with galvanized steel members	m2	180-240
Curtain walling with anodized aluminium members	m2	200-250
Extra for double glazed units and sun filter glass	m2	50-80
Extra for high quality finish to aluminium	m2	200-400
Patent glazing in vertical cladding to industrial type buildings	m2	75-100
Extra for double glazed units	m2	65-80
Aluminium sheeting profiled and insulated with inner lining	m2	100-180
Extra over for finishes to walls		
two coat cement and sand with pea gravel rough cast	m2	8-10
two coat 'Tyrolean' finish	m2	10-12
one coat hardwall plaster 5mm thick	m2	3-4
one coat hardwall plaster 13mm thick	m2	4-6

External walls (cont'd)	Unit	£
two coat hardwall plaster 13mm thick	m2	5-7
two coat lightweight plaster 10mm thick	m2	4-6
tile hanging including battens and felt	m2	25-35
boarding in Western Red Cedar	m2	28-35
shingles in Western Red Cedar	m2	25-35
exposed aggregates finish in concrete	m2	5-15
two coat emulsion paint	m2	3
one coat primer, one undercoat and one coat eggshell finish	m2	5
two base coats and coat 'Multicolour'	m2	6
lining paper (£0.75 per roll)	m2	2
woodchip paper (£1.20 per roll)	m2	3
flock paper (£6.50 per roll)	m2	4

WINDOWS AND EXTERNAL DOORS

Windows

	Unit	£
Softwood standard windows painted, single glazed	m2	120-150
Extra for double glazed	m2	40
Softwood windows, purpose made, painted, single glazed	m2	140-180
Extra for double glazed	m2	50
Steel standard windows with galvanized finish painted and single glazed	m2	130-160
Extra for double glazed	m2	40
Extra for self-finish colour coated	m2	5

	Unit	£
Steel windows, purpose made, colour coated	m2	180-220
Extra for double glazed	m2	50
Hardwood windows, purpose made, stained and single glazed	m2	170-230
Extra for double glazed	m2	50
uPVC windows purpose made	m2	300-350
Extra for sun-resistant glass	m2	25
Aluminium windows, purpose made, anodised, double glazed, hardwood frame	m2	240-300

External doors (including frames, ironmongery and finishes)

	Unit	£
Softwood external standard panelled doors	nr	175-225
Extra for glazed panels in decorative glass	nr	100-150
Hardwood external panelled door	nr	400-500
Solid core flush external door - single	nr	250-300
Solid core flush external door - pair	nr	350-400
Extra for glazed panels	nr	30-40
Extra for panic bolts, double doors	nr	100-150
Steel faced security flush external door	nr	1000-1500
Steel roller shutters	m2	120-200
Extra for electric motor operation	m2	50-100
Entrance doors and screens	m2	750-1000
Revolving doors - purpose made	nr	20000-25000

Windows and external doors (cont'd)	Unit	£
Rubber double doors	nr	1000-2000
Flexible strip curtains	nr	200-400

PARTITIONS AND INTERNAL WALLS

	Unit	£
Half brick wall	m2	23-27
Lightweight blocks 100mm thick	m2	21-23
Stud with plasterboard each side	m2	21-25
Proprietary manufacture plasterboard 65mm thick	m2	20-25
Metal stud and plasterboard one hour resistance	m2	30-40
Demountable steel partitions	m2	200-250
Aluminium partitions	m2	175-225
Glazed aluminium partitions	m2	90-120
Demountable aluminium partitions	m2	175-225
WC cubicles	nr	250-400

INTERNAL DOORS (including frames, ironmongery and finishes)

	Unit	£
Standard flush doors, hollow core	nr	75-120
Extra for hardwood face	nr	10-20
Standard flush doors solid core	nr	180-220
Extra for double doors	nr	75-125
Extra for hardwood face	nr	10-20
Fire check doors standard finish	nr	125-200
Purpose made panelled doors	nr	150-250

	Unit	£
Standard panelled softwood doors	nr	200-230
Extra for hardwood	nr	100-125

WALL FINISHES

		Hardwall two coats £	Lightweight two coats £
Plaster and emulsion paint	m2	10-20	7-12
With for three coats oil paint	m2	3-5	3-5
With for vinyl paper	m2	8-12	8-12

		Thickness	
		9.5mm £	12.5mm £
Plasterboard lining for direct decoration			
with emulsion paint	m2	7-10	8-10
with plastic coating: insulated	m2	9-12	9-12

Sheet linings on battens plugged to walls

	Unit	£
Supalux 9mm thick	m2	13-16
Decorative plywood 6mm thick	m2	12-15
Extra for flame retardant boards	m2	5
Fibreboard and hardboards	m2	6-12
'Formica' faced chipboards	m2	20-30
Gyproc wallboards 9.5mm thick finished with 'Drywall'	m2	8-12
Gyproc wallboards 12.5mm thick finished with 'Drywall'	m2	9-14
Extra for two layers 12.5mm	m2	6-7

Wall finishes (cont'd)	Unit	£
Softwood boarding 19mm thick	m2	15-20
Softwood boarding 25mm thick	m2	20-25
Hardwood panelled linings	m2	35-70
Tile wall finishes		
Ceramic tiles on backing of cement and sand	m2	25-40
High quality frost proof tiles with polysulphide mastic pointing	m2	40-60
FLOOR FINISHES		
Softwood tongued and grooved 25mm thick	m2	10-15
Chipboard tongued and grooved 22mm thick	m2	7-9
Hardwood tongued and grooved 22mm thick	m2	25-40
Screeds		
cement and sand, 50mm thick	m2	6-10
latex cement, 5mm thick	m2	4-6
granolithic, 25mm thick	m2	10-15
epoxy floor finish, 5mm thick	m2	25-30
extra heavy duty	m2	35-55
Tile paving		
quarry	m2	20-30
ceramic	m2	30-35
terrazzo	m2	40-60
vinyl	m2	8-10

	Unit	£
cork	m2	15-20
carpet	m2	25-30

Wood block flooring

herringbone pattern, sanded, wax polish

sapele	m2	30-40
oak	m2	40-45

Sheet materials

linoleum	m2	15-20
vinyl	m2	14-18
Extra for anti-static	m2	4-5
carpets including underlay	m2	15-30

CEILING FINISHES

	Unit	£
Lightweight plaster in two coats and emulsion	m2	8-10
Plasterboard soffit, 9.5mm thick	m2	8-10
'Thistle' skim coat and emulsion	m2	10-12
two coats of oil paint	m2	4
textured plaster finish ('Artex')	m2	4
sprayed acoustic plaster	m2	15-18

Suspended ceiling systems		£
Standard quality, exposed flanges to grid	m2	23-25
Extra for acoustic tiles	m2	5-8
Extra for high quality tiles	m2	10-15

Ceiling finishes (cont'd)	Unit	£
Aluminium suspended ceiling system - similar to 'Luxalon' with stove enamelled panels	m2	30-40
with 'egg crate' panels	m2	50-70
with patent decorative panels	m2	60-90

SANITARY FITTINGS (complete with water supply, taps and waste pipework)		White £	Coloured £
Lavatory basin with pedestal	nr	120	160
Low level WC suite	nr	130	160
Bath steel enamelled	nr	260	290
Bath, acrylic	nr	240	275
Shower with fireclay tray and curtains	nr	320	340
Stainless steel sink double drainer	nr	210	-
Lavatory basin in range	nr	150	200
Bowl type urinal, fireclay	nr	150	-
Drinking fountain	nr	250	-
Fireclay sinks for cleaners	nr	250	-
Slab urinals, 4 person	nr	850	-
Cast iron stack per floor	nr	150-200	-
PVC stack per floor	nr	60-100	-

HOT AND COLD WATER SERVICES

Copper hot and cold water services to domestic
or commercial sanitary fittings including all
building work: guide price £150-300 per point

	Unit	£

HEATING, VENTILATION AND ELECTRICAL SERVICES

See chapters 7 & 8

DRAINAGE

The following rates include for machine excavation, disposal and backfilling of excavated material and pipe fittings

Vitrified clay pipes laid in trench 500mm deep on 150mm granular bed and haunching, nominal bore

	Unit	£
100mm 'Supersleve' with push-fit joints	m	13-15
100mm 'Standard' pipes with mortar joints	m	14-16
Extra for concrete bed and haunching	m	6-8
150mm 'Hepsleve' with push-fit sleeve joints	m	15-17
150mm Hepseal with push-fit spigot and socket joints	m	18-20
Extra for 150mm concrete bed and surround	m	18-20
225mm 'Hepseal' pipes as before	m	25-27
Extra for concrete bed and haunch	m	18-20
300mm 'Hepseal' pipes as before	m	38-40
Extra for 150mm granular bed and surround	m	20-24

Cast iron pipes laid in trench 500mm deep on 150mm granular bed and haunching

	Unit	£
100mm 'Time saver' mechanical joints	m	30-32

Drainage (cont'd)	Unit	£
100mm Caulked lead joints	m	38-40
Extra for 150mm concrete bed and surround	m	18-20
150mm 'Time saver' mechanical joints	m	51-55
150mm Caulked lead joints	m	58-62
Extra for 150mm granular bed and surround	m	4-6

Add to foregoing rates for deeper trenches

1000mm deep; pipes up to 200mm bore	m	6-8
2000mm deep; pipes up to 225mm bore	m	12-14
3000mm deep; pipes up to 300mm bore	m	14-16

Add to foregoing rates for excavating by hand

500mm deep; pipes up to 200mm bore	m	4-6
1000mm deep; pipes up to 200mm bore	m	6-8
2000mm deep; pipes up to 225mm bore	m	25-30

Manholes

Brick manhole including machine excavation, concrete base, engineering brickwork (class 'B') concrete cover slab, 600 x 600 cast iron medium duty cover, channels and benchings

600 x 450 x 1000mm deep	nr	250-300
Extra for heavy duty triangular cover	nr	50-70
Add or deduct for depth variations per 100mm		10-12
900 x 600 x 1500mm deep	nr	450-500

	Unit	£
Add or deduct for depth variations per 100mm		12-15
1250 x 750 x 2000mm deep	nr	850-900
Add or deduct for depth variation per 100mm		35-40
1500 x 900 x 2500mm deep	nr	1000-1100
Add or deduct for depth variations per 100mm		20-30

Precast concrete ring manhole including machine excavation, concrete base, unreinforced concrete rings, heavy duty concrete cover slab with brickwork shaft 600 x 600 four courses high and heavy duty road manhole cover

	Unit	£
675mm shaft x 1000mm deep	nr	350-400
Add or deduct for depth variation per 100mm		7-10
900mm shaft x 2000mm deep	nr	550-600
Add or deduct for depth variations per 100mm		10-12
1200mm shaft x 3000mm deep	nr	900-1000
Add or deduct for depth variations per 100mm		25-30

Precast concrete ring manholes including machine excavation, concrete base, reinforced concrete rings, heavy duty concrete cover slab with brickwork shaft 600 x 600 four courses high and heavy duty road manhole cover.

	Unit	£
1350mm shaft, 2000mm deep	nr	750-800
Add or deduct for variation in depth 100mm		20-25

Drainage (cont'd)	Unit	£
1500mm shaft, 2500mm deep	nr	900-1000
Add or deduct for variation in depth 100mm		25-30
1800mm shaft 3000mm deep	nr	1100-1200
Add or deduct for variations in depth 100mm		30-35

Inspection chambers

£

UPVC inspection chambers, 450mm
diameter, single seal cast iron
cover and frame with 4nr 100mm
diameter outlets, depth

500mm	nr	110-130
750mm	nr	120-140
950mm	nr	130-150

Gullies including excavation and concrete

Concrete road gulley, heavy duty grating	nr	160-180
Stoneware yard gulley and grating	nr	80-100
Cast iron yard gulley and grating	nr	140-160
Rainwater gulley and grating	nr	30-40

EXTERNAL WORKS

Excavation and disposal to formation,
150mm hardcore bed, blinding,
compaction for surface paving

Precast concrete paving flags, 50mm thick	m2	14-16
Insitu concrete, 100mm thick	m2	10-12
Brick paviours, 230 x 115 x 40mm thick	m2	24-26

	Unit	£
Granite setts, 200 x 100 x 100mm thick	m2	45-50
York stone paving	m2	60-65
Cobblestones, 75mm thick	m2	35-40
Gravel, 50mm thick	m2	7-9
Tarmac, two layers, 65mm thick	m2	8-10

Roads

Estate roads including excavation and disposal to formation, base course sub base and wearing surfaces in two layers 75mm thick bitumen macadam with 127 x 254mm precast concrete kerbs each side

4.5m wide	m	125-130
7.5m wide	m	190-230

Part Two

Civil Engineering Work

Class A: GENERAL ITEMS

The pricing of this section is highly subjective and the information set out below should be used with the knowledge that there are as many different approaches to the pricing of general items and bill rates as there are civil engineering estimators.

Analysis of the general items in tenders for civil projects show a proportion of between 15% and 40% of the total bill even when the overall level of the tenders are similar. This is mainly due to different pricing strategies adopted by estimators.

The general items listed below are based upon the needs of a civil project whose contract value is approximately £5m with an 18 month (78 weeks) contract period. The list of items given is not intended to be exhaustive.

Contractual requirements

Performance bond

1% for construction period x 1.5 years x £3m	45,000	
3/4% for maintenance period x 1 year x £3m	22,500	67,500

Insurance of the Works

1½% x £3m	45,000	
Inflation say 1½% x 5½% x £3m	2,250	
Extra work say 1½% x 10% x £3m	4,500	51,750

Insurance of construction plant

included in hire charges		nil
Carried forward	£	119,250

Contractual requirements (cont'd)

Brought forward	£	119,250

Insurance against damage to persons
and property

included in head office overheads		nil

Specified requirements

Offices for Engineer's staff

erect	250	
maintain and operate (100 weeks x £75)	7,500	
remove	<u>250</u>	8,000

Laboratory for Engineer's staff

erect	200	
maintain and operate (50 weeks x £50)	2,500	
remove	<u>200</u>	2,900

Cabins for Engineer's staff

erect	200	
maintain and operate (100 weeks x £50)	5,000	
remove	<u>200</u>	5,400

Services for the Engineer

1800cc car (100 weeks x £160)	16,000	
landrover (78 weeks x £150)	11,700	
telephone, installation	150	
telephone, maintain and operate (100 weeks x £50)	<u>5,000</u>	<u>32,850</u>

Carried forward	£	168,400

Brought forward	£	168,400

Equipment for the Engineer

office equipment (100 weeks x £50) comprising	5,000	

1 word processor
2 desks
2 tables
1 conference table
8 chairs
2 filing cabinets
sundries

laboratory equipment (50 weeks x £50)	2,500	
surveying equipment (78 weeks x £40)	3,120	10,620

Attendance upon the Engineer		
driver (50 weeks x £240)	12,000	
chainman (78 weeks x £200)	15,600	
laboratory assistant, part time (30 x £300)	9,000	36,600

Testing of materials (included)		nil
Testing of works (included)		nil

Temporary works

traffic signals (30 weeks @ £20)	600	
cleaning roads (40 weeks @ £300)	12,000	
progress photographs	1,000	
temporary lighting (40 weeks @ £40)	1,600	
temporary water supply, connection	1,000	
temporary water supply, pipework (200m x £4)	800	
temporary water supply (2,000,000 litres x 40p per 1000)	800	
temporary water supply, remove	200	
hardstanding (500m2 x £8)	4,000	
hardstanding, remove	500	21,950

Carried forward		236,610

Brought forward	£	236,610

Method Related Charges

Offices for Contractor

erect	350	
maintain and operate (100 weeks x £100)	10,000	
remove	300	

Cabins for Contractor

erect	250	
maintain and operate (78 weeks x £40)	3,120	
remove	200	

Stores for Contractor

erect	250	
maintain and operate (100 weeks @ £40)	4,000	
remove	200	

Canteens and messroom for Contractor

erect	400	
maintain and operate (78 weeks x £70)	5,460	
remove	250	

Electricity

install	1,000	
maintain (100 weeks x £40)	4,000	

Supervision, administration

agent 90 weeks @ £500	45,000	
assistant agents (2) 156 weeks @ £450	70,200	
inspectors (2) 156 weeks @ £350	54,600	
setting out engineer 30 weeks @ £400	12,000	
quantity surveyor 110 weeks @ £450	49,500	
section foremen (4) 312 weeks @ £350	109,200	
timekeeper/wages clerk 78 weeks @ £250	19,500	

Carried forward	£	389,780	236,610

	£		
Brought forward	£	389,780	236,610
storekeeper 78 weeks @ £250		19,500	
watchman 100 weeks @ £250		25,000	
tea boy 78 weeks @ £200		15,600	
Supervision, offloading and cleaning gang			
labourers (2) 140 weeks @ £250		35,000	484,880
TOTAL	£		721,490

CLASS B: GROUND INVESTIGATION	Unit	£
Trial pits size 1 x 2m, not in rock maximum depth		
not exceeding 1m	nr	15
1-2m	nr	20
2-3m	nr	30
3-5m	nr	40
5-10m	nr	60
Trial pits size 1 x 2m, partly in rock, maximum depth		
not exceeding 1m	nr	30
1-2m	nr	40
2-3m	nr	60
3-5m	nr	80
5-10m	nr	120
Trial pits size 1 x 2m, in rock, maximum depth		
not exceeding 1m	nr	60
1-2m	nr	120
2-3m	nr	180

Ground investigation (cont'd)	Unit	£
3-5m	nr	300
5-10m	nr	450
Light percussion boreholes, 150mm diameter	nr	75
depth not exceeding 5m	m	15
5-10m	m	20
10-20m	m	35
20-30m	m	50
30-40m	m	70
Rotary drilled boreholes, 150mm diameter without core recovery	nr	75
depth not exceeding 5m	m	15
5-10m	m	18
10-20m	m	25
20-30m	m	30
30-40m	m	50
Rotary drilled boreholes, 75mm diameter, with core recovery		
depth not exceeding 5m	m	50
5-10m	m	60
10-20m	m	70
20-30m	m	80
30-40m	m	90

CLASS C: GEOTECHNICAL AND OTHER SPECIALIST PROCESSES

Drilling

An allowance of £6,000 should be made for the establishment and removal of plant and equipment to carry out drilling operations.

	Depth				
	ne 5m £/m	5-10m £/m	10-20m £/m	20-30m £/m	30-40m £/m
Drilling for grout holes through material other than rock					
vertically downwards	12	15	17	20	22
downwards at an angle of 0-45^{0} to the vertical	13	16	18	21	23
horizontally or downwards at an angle less than 45^{0} to the horizontal	14	17	19	22	24
upwards at an angle 0-45^{0} to the horizontal	18	22	24	27	30
upwards at an angle less than 45^{0} to the vertical	20	24	26	30	32

Geotechnical and other specialist
processes (cont'd)

	Depth				
	ne 5m £/m	5-10m £/m	10-20m £/m	20-30m £/m	30-40m £/m
Drilling for grout holes through rock					
vertically downwards	18	21	23	25	28
downwards at an angle of 0-45° to the vertical	19	22	24	26	29
horizontally or downwards at an angle less than 45° to the horizontal	20	23	25	27	30
upwards at an angle 0-45° to the horizontal	24	26	29	31	34
upwards at an angle less than 45° to the vertical	26	28	31	33	38

Grout materials and injections

An allowance of £6,000 should be made for the establishment and
renewal of plant and equipment to carry out grouting operations.

Materials	Unit	£
cement bentonite (2:1)	t	85
cement PFA	t	55
sand	t	15
pea gravel	t	15
bentonite	t	175

	Unit	£
Injections		
number of holes	nr	50

Diaphragm walls

It is assumed in the following rates that a minimum of 3000 m3 of excavation is required. An allowance of £40,000 should be made for the establishment and removal of plant and equipment to carry out the work.

	Unit	£
Excavation in material other than rock or artificial hard material		
maximum depth not exceeding 5m	m3	110
maximum depth 5-10m	m3	120
maximum depth 10-15m	m3	135
maximum depth 15-20m	m3	150
Concrete designed mix to BS5328; grade 20; ordinary portland cement to BS12; 20mm aggregate to BS882; walls 1000mm thick	m3	85
High yield bar reinforcement to BS4449		
nominal size 12mm	t	590
nominal size 16mm	t	540
nominal size 20mm	t	510
nominal size 25mm	t	490
Waterproof joints	sum	200
Concrete guide walls either side of excavation; each wall 1000mm wide x 500mm deep	m	150

Ground anchorages

It is assumed in the following rates that a minimum of 75 nr
anchors are to be installed and an allowance of £4,000 should
be made for the establishment and removal of plant and equipment.

Ground anchorages, number in material other than rock to a maximum 10m depth; load 50 tonne	Unit	£
temporary	nr	90
temporary with single corrosion protection	nr	90
temporary with double corrosion protection	nr	90
permanent	nr	90
permanent with single corrosion protection	nr	90
permanent with double corrosion protection	nr	90
Total length of tendon in material other than rock		
temporary	m	65
temporary with single corrosion protection	m	70
temporary with double corrosion protection	m	75
permanent	m	90
permanent with single corrosion protection	m	95
permanent with double corrosion protection	m	100

	Unit	£
Ground anchorages, number in material which includes rock to a maximum 10m depth; load 50 tonne		
temporary	nr	115
temporary with single corrosion protection	nr	115
temporary with double corrosion protection	nr	115
permanent	nr	115
permanent with single corrosion protection	nr	115
permanent with double corrosion protection	nr	115
Total length of tendon in material which includes rock		
temporary	m	80
temporary with single corrosion protection	m	85
temporary with double corrosion protection	m	90
permanent	m	105
permanent with single corrosion protection	m	110
permanent with double corrosion protection	m	115

Sand, band and wick drains

It is assumed in the following rates that a minimum of 100 vertical drains are to be installed and an allowance of £6,000 should be made for the establishment and removal of plant and equipment.

	Unit	£
Number of drains	nr	60
Pre-drilled holes	nr	60
Drains of maximum depth not exceeding 10m		
cross section 100-200mm	m	6
cross section 200-300mm	m	7
cross section 300-400mm	m	9
Drains of maximum depth 10-15m		
cross section 100-200mm	m	7
cross section 200-300mm	m	8
cross section 300-400mm	m	10
Drains of maximum depth 15-20m		
cross section 100-200mm	m	8
cross section 200-300mm	m	9
cross section 300-400mm	m	11

CLASS D: DEMOLITION AND SITE CLEARANCE

General clearance

General site clearance of areas		
free from major obstructions	ha	600
woods, small trees and shrubs	ha	1500

	Unit	£
Pull down trees (stumps measured separately) girth		
500mm-1m	nr	20
1-2m	nr	40
2-3m	nr	150
3-5m	nr	800
Grub up stumps and backfill with topsoil, diameter		
150-500mm	nr	20
500mm-1m	nr	40
1-2m	nr	60
Demolish buildings		
brickwork		
volume 50-100m3	sum	300
volume 250-500m3	sum	1250
volume 1000-2500m3	sum	2500
concrete		
volume 50-100m3	sum	400
volume 250-500m3	sum	1750
volume 1000-2500m3	sum	10,000
Clay drains depth 1.5m including stone bed and surround	m	5
Concrete pipe depth 2m including concrete bed and surround	m	8

CLASS E - EARTHWORKS

Dredging

It is extremely difficult to give even approximate cost information about excavation by dredging. The method used (cutter suction dredger, barge mounted excavator or grab hopper are some of the options), the depth of water and the disposal arrangements are all key factors.

The cost per cubic metre of dredging solid material should be in the range of £2 to £7 per cubic metre but specialist advice should be obtained even at the budget estimate stage.

		Average Condition £	Topsoil £	Stiff Clay £	Chalk £	Roc £
General excavation to reduce levels, maximum depth						
not exceeding 0.25m	m3	2.80	2.50	4.20	6.25	16.8
0.25-0.5m	m3	2.80	2.40	4.20	6.25	16.8
0.5-1m	m3	3.50	-	5.25	8.75	21.0
1-2m	m3	4.00	-	6.00	10.00	24.0
2-5m	m3	6.00	-	9.00	15.00	36.0
Excavation for foundation, maximum depth						
not exceeding 0.25m	m3	3.80	3.50	5.70	9.50	22.8
0.25-0.5m	m3	3.80	3.70	5.70	9.50	22.8
0.5-1m	m3	4.50	-	6.75	11.25	27.0
1-2m	m3	5.00	-	7.50	12.50	30.0
2-5m	m3	6.00	-	9.00	15.00	36.0

	Unit	£
Disposal of excavated material		
deposited on site 100m distance	m3	2
deposited on site 300m distance	m3	3
deposited off site 1km distance including tipping fees	m3	5
deposited off site 5km distance including tipping fees	m3	7
Filling material compacted in layers		
surplus excavated material	m3	2
imported topsoil	m3	11
imported granular material (DTp Type 1)	m3	16
imported granular material (DTp Type 2)	m3	14

CLASS F: IN SITU CONCRETE

Provision of concrete

Standard mix to BS 5328

	Unit	£
ST3, ordinary portland cement to BS 12, 20mm aggregate to BS 882	m3	48

Designed mix to BS 5328

	Unit	£
grade C20, sulphate resisting cement to BS 4027, 20mm aggregate to BS 882	m3	52

Insitu concrete (cont'd)	Unit	£
grade F4, ordinary portland cement to BS 12, 14mm aggregate to BS 882	m3	50

Placing of mass concrete

Blinding, thickness not exceeding 150mm	m3	10

Bases, footings, pile caps and ground slabs

thickness, 150-300mm	m3	12
thickness exceeding 500mm	m3	9

Placing of reinforced concrete

Suspended slabs

thickness 150-300mm	m3	13
thickness 300-500mm	m3	12

Walls, thickness 300-500mm	m3	12

Columns and piers, cross sectional area 0.25-1m2	m3	15

CLASS G: CONCRETE ANCILLARIES

Formwork, rough finish, width exceeding 1.22m

horizontal	m2	18
vertical	m2	22
curved to 2m radius in one plane	m2	35

Formwork, fair finish, width exceeding 1.22m

horizontal	m2	20
vertical	m2	24

	Unit	£
urved to 2m radius in one plane	m2	38
einforcement, mild steel bars 4449, diameter		
mm	t	860
2mm	t	760
6mm	t	720
0mm	t	700
5mm	t	690
2mm	t	680
0mm	t	660
gh yield steel bars BS 4461 ameter		
mm	t	860
2mm	t	780
6mm	t	740
0mm	t	700
5mm	t	690
2mm	t	680
0mm	t	670
eel fabric BS4483 weight		
-4 kg/m2, C385	m2	4
-5 kg/m2, B385	m2	5
-6 kg/m2, B503	m2	6
-7 kg/m2, A393	m2	7

Joints	Unit	£
Open surface plain with cork filler width 0.5-1m, thickness		
10mm	m2	25
20mm	m2	30
25mm	m2	40
Formed surface plain with cork filler width 0.5-1m, thickness		
10mm	m2	30
20mm	m2	35
25mm	m2	45

CLASS H: PRECAST CONCRETE

Prestressed pre-tensioned members, concrete (1:2:4 20mm aggregate)

Beams size		
100 x 65 x 1500mm	nr	20
200 x 65 x 2000mm	nr	30
250 x 100 x 2500mm	nr	50

Slabs, superimposed loads maximum 5 kg/m2, size		
100 x 400 x 6000mm	nr	110
100 x 1200 x 6000mm	nr	180
100 x 2400 x 6000mm	nr	360
150 x 400 x 6000mm	nr	130
150 x 1200 x 6000mm	nr	210
150 x 2400 x 6000mm	nr	400

	Unit	£
Copings, sills and weir blocks, weathered and throated, size		
150 x 75mm	m	11
200 x 75mm	m	13
300 x 75mm	m	16

CLASSES I, J, K and L DRAINAGE
Excavation

Excavating trenches for pipes, backfilling and removing surplus
excavated material from site per linear metre.

Pipe diameter mm

Excavation depth	150 £	225 £	300 £	375 £	400 £	450 £	525 £	600 £	900 £	1200 £	1500 £
500mm	3	4	-	-	-	-	-	-	-	-	-
750mm	5	6	7	-	-	-	-	-	-	-	-
1000mm	7	9	11	-	-	-	-	-	-	-	-
1250mm	8	9	10	-	-	-	-	-	-	-	-
1500mm	9	12	14	16	28	32	34	37	40	-	-
1750mm	10	12	13	14	17	18	19	21	30	-	-
2000mm	11	14	17	18	30	35	38	41	44	63	75
2500mm	13	16	18	20	33	36	40	43	47	66	100
3000mm	15	18	20	23	35	39	43	47	51	72	108
3500mm	18	23	25	27	40	43	48	55	60	80	115
4000mm	20	26	30	33	45	50	58	66	72	94	127
4500mm	30	35	40	41	53	60	70	80	87	112	130
5000mm	38	42	50	51	63	70	80	91	103	128	150
5500mm	45	53	60	63	75	80	94	107	119	144	168
6000mm	55	65	75	78	90	95	105	120	135	160	187

	Unit	£
Beds, haunches and surrounds		
Sand bed 150mm thick to pipe nominal bore		
150mm	m	3.10
225mm	m	3.60
300mm	m	4.45
375mm	m	5.40
400mm	m	5.70
450mm	m	6.50
525mm	m	7.10
600mm	m	7.80
900mm	m	9.90
1200mm	m	12.00
1500mm	m	15.30
Granular material, 10mm nominal size, bed 150mm thick to pipe nominal bore		
150mm	m	2.60
225mm	m	3.30
300mm	m	4.10
375mm	m	4.60
400mm	m	5.20
450mm	m	5.90
525mm	m	7.10

Beds, haunches and surrounds (cont'd)	Unit	£
600mm	m	7.80
900mm	m	8.90
1200mm	m	10.50
1500mm	m	13.10

Granular material, 10mm nominal
size, bed and surround to pipe
nominal bore

150mm	m	5.70
225mm	m	6.80
300mm	m	8.50
375mm	m	10.20
400mm	m	11.00
450mm	m	12.70
525mm	m	14.00
600mm	m	15.60
900mm	m	19.40
1200mm	m	27.30
1500mm	m	33.00

Concrete, mix 11.5 N/mm2 40mm
aggregate, bed to pipe nominal bore

150mm	m	7.80
225mm	m	9.20
300mm	m	10.50
375mm	m	12.40

	Unit	£
400mm	m	13.30
450mm	m	13.50
525mm	m	14.65
600mm	m	15.80
900mm	m	19.70
1200mm	m	23.60
1500mm	m	27.10

Concrete, mix 11.5 N/mm2 40mm
aggregate, bed and haunch to pipe
nominal bore

150mm	m	9.80
225mm	m	12.00
300mm	m	15.80
375mm	m	17.80
400mm	m	19.50
450mm	m	22.50
525mm	m	23.50
600mm	m	24.90
900mm	m	38.00
1200mm	m	46.50
1500mm	m	55.00

Concrete, mix 11.5 N/mm2 40mm
aggregate, bed and surround to pipe
nominal bore

150mm	m	18.60

Beds, haunches and surrounds (cont'd)	Unit	£
225mm	m	22.40
300mm	m	26.50
375mm	m	30.00
400mm	m	31.20
450mm	m	35.20
525mm	m	38.80
600mm	m	42.40
900mm	m	59.90
1200mm	m	89.00
1500mm	m	100.00

Pipes laid in trench

Vitrified clay to BS65, spigot and
socket joints with sealing ring
nominal bore

150mm	m	10
225mm	m	17
300mm	m	26
400mm	m	46
450mm	m	60

Ductile spun iron to BS4772 with
Tyton joints, nominal bore

150mm	m	18
250mm	m	29
350mm	m	45

	Unit	£
450mm	m	62
600mm	m	92
uPVC to BS 3506 with ring seal sockets, nominal bore		
110mm	m	7
160mm	m	11
200mm	m	16
250mm	m	24
Concrete pipe to BS556, Class H, nominal bore,		
375mm	m	26
450mm	m	30
525mm	m	36
750mm	m	60
900mm	m	75
1200mm	m	125
1500mm	m	185
Concrete pipe to BS556, Class M, nominal bore,		
300mm	m	20
375mm	m	26
450mm	m	30
525mm	m	35
750mm	m	55
900mm	m	74

Pipes laid in trench (cont'd)	Unit	£
1200mm	m	120
1500mm	m	175

Concrete pipe to BS556, Class L, nominal bore,

	Unit	£
300mm	m	20
375mm	m	26
450mm	m	30
525mm	m	35
750mm	m	54
900mm	m	72
1200mm	m	110
1500mm	m	170

Manholes

Depth

Brick manhole comprising in situ concrete base, channels and benching, precast concrete cover slabs, cast iron steps and medium duty cover size	1m £	1.5m £	2m £	2.5m £	3m £	4m £	5m £
750 x 600mm	550	700	900	1100	-	-	-
1200 x 750mm	-	-	-	1300	1500	1800	2100

Precast concrete manhole comprising in situ concrete base, channels and benching precast concrete rings, cover slab, cast iron steps/ladders and heavy duty cover, diameter

	1m £	1.5m £	2m £	2.5m £	3m £	4m £	5m £
675mm	300	350	400	460	530	630	830
900mm	385	450	500	565	635	750	950
1050mm	450	600	650	750	825	950	1200
1200mm	-	750	700	850	1000	1250	1500
1500mm	-	900	1050	1200	1350	1475	1750
1800mm	-	1000	1175	1350	1600	2000	2500

Gullies

	Unit	£
Vitrified clay road gully, 480mm diameter x 900 mm deep, including excavation, concrete surround, Class B engineering brick seating and cast iron grating	nr	365
Precast concrete road gully, 375mm diameter x 900 mm deep, including excavation, concrete surround, Class B engineering brick seating and cast iron grating	nr	140

French drains

	Unit	£
All French and rubble drains with Type A filter material	m3	20

Rectangular section ditches unlined cross sectional area

	Unit	£
0.25-0.5m2	m	7
0.5-0.75m2	m	9

French drains (cont'd)	Unit	£
0.75-1m2	m	11
1-1.5m2	m	14
1.5-2m2	m	18

Rectangular section ditches lined with Filtram, cross sectional area

0.25-0.5m2	m	9
0.5-0.75m2	m	12
0.75-1m2	m	15
1-1.5m2	m	18
1.5-2m2	m	26

Trenches for pipes or cable not to be laid by the Contractor, cross sectional area

0.25-0.5m2	m	6
0.5-0.75m2	m	8
0.75-1m2	m	10
1-5m2	m	13
1.5-2m2	m	16

One way cable ducts, 100mm diameter in trench depth not exceeding

1.5m	m	16
1.5-2m	m	20
2-2.5m	m	25
2.5-3m	m	30

	Unit	£
Two way cable ducts, 100mm diameter in trench depth not exceeding		
1.5m	m	30
1.5-2m	m	38
2-2.5m	m	45
2.5-3m	m	55

Reinstatement

	Unit	£
Breaking up and temporary reinstatement of trench for pipe nominal bore not exceeding 300mm		
grassland	m	2
road, 75mm thick bituminous macadam and base under	m	22
road, 100 mm thick bituminous macadam and base under	m	26
road, 150mm thick bituminous macadam and base under	m	32
pavement, 50mm thick bituminous macadam and base under	m	14

CLASS M: STRUCTURAL METALWORK

Fabrication of members for frames	Unit	£
columns	t	880
beams	t	850
portal frames	t	830
trusses and built up girders	t	900
bracings, purlins and cladding rails	t	860

Structural metalwork (cont'd)	Unit	£
anchorages and holding down assemblies	t	1000
permanent erection of members for frames	t	200
Site bolts		
black	t	1800
HSFG general grade	t	1900
HSFG higher grade	t	2200
HSFG load indicating or load limit	t	2400
Offsite surface treatment		
blast cleaning	t	75
wire brushing	t	110
galvanizing	t	200
one coat chromate primer	t	130

CLASS N: MISCELLANEOUS METALWORK

Stairways and landings	t	2000
Walkways and platforms	t	1800
Cat ladder in galvanized steel rungs at 300mm centres, strings extended to form handrail, 450mm wide, length		
3000mm	nr	600
4000mm	nr	800
5000mm	nr	1000
6000mm	nr	1200

	Unit	£
7000mm	nr	1400
8000mm	nr	1600
9000mm	nr	1800
10000mm	nr	2000
Guard cage to cat ladder	m	40

Galvanized steel staircase 900mm wide with chequer plate treads balustrade one side, supported on universal columns

5500mm going, 3000mm rise, 16 treads and one landing	nr	2400
10000mm going, 5000mm rise, 16 treads and two landings	nr	3500

Galvanized tubular handrail, 1050mm high, standards at 2000mm centres, with middle rail	m	75
Galvanized flat section handrail and members, standards at 1000mm centres, infilled with square vertical bars at 100mm centres	m	110

Safety fencing

Tensioned corrugated to DTp Clause 409 with 'Z' section steel posts set in concrete

single side	m	40
double sided	m	50

| Untensioned corrugated to DTp Clause 412, single sided with timber posts | m | 35 |

	Unit	£
Miscellaneous framing		
Angle section		
150 x 75 x 10mm	m	12
100 x 100 x 10mm	m	11
150 x 150 x 12mm	m	15
Channel section		
150 x 75 x 10mm	m	15
250 x 75 x 16mm	m	22
Flooring		
Galvanized mild steel 'Durbar' pattern plate 8mm thick	m2	90
Galvanized open grid flooring 50mm thick	m2	150
CLASS O: TIMBER		
Greenheart timber in marine works		
100 x 75mm	m	16
150 x 75mm	m	22
200 x 200mm	m	75
200 x 300mm	m	80
300 x 300mm	m	100
600 x 600mm	m	300
Wrought softwood in marine work		
100 x 75mm	m	10
150 x 75mm	m	12

	Unit	£
200 x 200mm	m	25
200 x 300mm	m	35
300 x 300mm	m	40
Hardwood decking, thickness		
50mm	m2	65
75mm	m2	80
100mm	m2	100
Softwood decking, thickness		
50mm	m2	35
75mm	m2	40
100mm	m2	50
Coach screws, length		
75mm	nr	2
100mm	nr	3
150mm	nr	4
Blackbolts, nuts and washers, length		
100mm	nr	2
150mm	nr	3
200mm	nr	4

CLASS P: PILING

There are many different types of piling and the following have been included in this section

1. Bored cast in place concrete piles
2. Driven cast in place concrete piles
3. Pre-formed concrete piles
4. Isolated steel piles
5. Interlocking steel sheet piles

The costs are based upon constructing a minimum of 50 piles and the establishing and dismantling of equipment is shown separately.

Bored cast in place concrete piles

Cost of rig, set up and removal from site for £5500 for 50 piles, £10,000 for 100 piles.

| | Unit | Diameter of pile mm | | | |
		300	600	900	1200
Depth bored		£	£	£	£
10m	m	12	15	25	45
15m	m	10	14	22	42
20m	m	9	13	20	38
Concrete	m	15	34	60	110

Driven cast in place concrete piles

Cost of rig, set up and removal from site - £3250 for 50 piles, £6000 for 100 piles

Depth bored					
10m	m	10	12	14	20
15m	m	8	10	13	18
20m	m	7	9	12	17
Concrete	m	15	34	60	110

Preformed concrete piles

		Cross-sectional area mm		
		300x300	500x500	700x700
Design load	tonne	50	75	100
		£	£	£
Depth of pile				
10m	m	30	35	45
15m	m	27	32	42
20m	m	23	30	40

Add for transport of rig and piles £4000 - £5000 per job

Steel sheet piling

		1N	2N	3N	4N
		£	£	£	£
Larsen/Frodingham sections	m2	50	60	70	80
Extra for corners	m	30	30	30	30
Extra for junction	m	40	40	40	40

Add for transport of rig and piles, £3000-£4000 per job

Noise abatement requirements, £900-£1500 per job

	Unit	£
CLASS R: ROADS AND PAVINGS		
Sub-bases flexible road bases and surfacing		
Hardcore road base depth 300mm	m3	15
Hardcore road base, depth		
100mm depth	m2	2
150mm depth	m2	3
Granular material, DTp type 1, depth		
100mm	m2	3
200mm	m2	5
300mm	m3	10
Granular material DTp type 2, depth 300mm	m3	14
Wet mix macadam DTp clause 808 base course, depth		
100mm	m2	3
200mm	m2	5
Dense bitumen macadam, DTp clause 908		
14mm aggregate, depth		
30mm wearing course	m2	3
40mm wearing course	m2	4
40mm aggregate, depth		
60mm base course	m2	5
80mm base course	m2	6

	Unit	£
Concrete pavements		
Carriageway slabs, grade C20, depth		
150mm	m3	60
150-350mm	m3	58
Carriageway slabs, DTp Specification C30 depth		
180mm	m2	14
250mm	m2	19
Steel fabric reinforcement to BS4483		
reference A142 2.22 kgs/m2	m2	4
reference B503 5.93 kgs/m2	m2	7
Waterproof membranes below concrete pavements, plastic sheeting, 1200 gauge	m2	2
Joints in concrete pavements		
Longitudinal joints, 10mm diameter x 750mm long mild steel dowels at 750mm centres, sealed with polysulphide, depth		
150mm	m	30
220mm	m	32
250mm	m	32

	Unit	£

Kerbs, channels and edgings

Precast concrete kerbs to BS340
straight or curved to radius
exceeding 12m

fig 6 150 x 305mm	m	12
fig 7 125 x 255mm	m	10

CLASS S: RAIL TRACK

Track foundations

Bottom ballast granite, crushed, graded 50-25mm	m3	28
Top ballast granite, crushed, graded 50-25mm	m3	32

Taking up track and turnouts, dismantle and stack

Bullhead or flat bottom rail

plain track, timber sleepers, fishplate joints	m	4
turnouts, timber sleepers, fishplate joints	nr	200
Extra for concrete sleepers	m	2

Sundries

buffer stops, weight 2-3 tonnes	nr	60

Lifting packing and slewing

Bullhead rail track on timber sleepers track length 10m maximum slew 300mm, maximum lift 100mm	nr	120
Extra for concrete sleepers	nr	10
Turnout on timber sleepers	nr	320

	Unit	£
Supplying only plain line material		
Bullhead rails; for joints or welded track		
mass 40-50 kg/m, section reference 95R	t	600
Sleepers		
softwood timber, 250 x 125 x 2600mm long	nr	25
hardwood timber, 250 x 125 x 2600mm long	nr	35
concrete sleepers, type 'F27' with 2 nr cast iron 'Pandrol' fittings cast in	nr	45
Fittings		
Chairs, cast iron 'CC' pattern complete	nr	30
Fish plates, standard set complete	nr	25
Fish plates, insulated set complete	nr	80
Switches and crossings		
turnouts	nr	9000-14,000
diamond crossings	nr	8000-11,500
Sundries		
buffer stops, 2-2.5 tonnes	nr	1000-1,500
Laying only plain line material		
Bullhead rails		
plain track, mass 40-50 kg/m fish plate joints, timber sleepers	m	18
welded joints, concrete sleepers	m	30

Laying only plain line material (cont'd)	Unit	£
form curve in plain track, radius not exceeding 300mm	m	6
turnout, standard type on timber sleepers	nr	1500
buffer stop, single rake	nr	150
'Thermit' weld on Bullhead rail	nr	100

CLASS T: TUNNELS

There are many different methods of boring and constructing tunnels so the following rates should be treated with caution. For costs on specific jobs the advice of a tunnelling contractor should be sought.

Excavation

Tunnels in rock; straight

diameter 1.8m	m3	120

Tunnels in clay; straight

diameter 1.8m	m3	80

Shafts in rock; vertical

diameter 3.0m	m3	100

Shafts in clay; vertical

diameter 3.0m	m3	70

Other cavities in rock

diameter 3.0m	m3	120

Other cavities in clay

diameter 3.0m	m3	70

	Unit	£
Excavated surfaces in rock		
cement grout	m2	15
Excavated surfaces in clay		
PFA/OPC grout (1:3)	m2	9
In situ lining to shafts; vertical		
Cast concrete grade C20, primary		
diameter 2.13m	m3	95
Cast concrete grade C20; secondary		
diameter 2.13m	m3	100
Formwork; rough finish		
diameter 2.13m	m2	18
Formwork; smooth finish		
diameter 2.13m	m2	24
Pre-formed segmental linings to tunnels		
Precast concrete bolted flanged rings		
diameter 2.74m special sealing gaskets	nr	550
diameter 3.05m standard gaskets	nr	500
Pre-formed segmental linings to shafts		
Precast concrete bolted flanged rings		
diameter 4.27m	nr	800
diameter 6.48m	nr	2000

	Unit	£

CLASS U: BRICKWORK, BLOCKWORK AND MASONRY

Common brickwork, BS3921, PC £125 per thousand in cement mortar (1:3)

in vertical walls

102mm thick	m2	30
215mm thick	m2	60
327mm thick	m2	75
440mm thick	m2	95

in columns and piers

215 x 215mm	m	15
327 x 327mm	m	30
440 x 440mm	m	50

Facing brickwork, PC £300 per thousand in coloured cement lime mortar (1:1:6)

in vertical walls in Flemish bond

102mm thick	m2	55
215mm thick	m2	100

in vertical curved walls in English bond

102mm thick	m2	65
215mm thick	m2	120
327mm thick	m2	150

	Unit	£
Engineering brickwork, PC £200 per thousand in cement mortar (1:3)		
in vertical walls in English bond		
215mm thick	m2	80
327mm thick	m2	120
440mm thick	m2	150
Engineering brickwork; PC £200 per thousand in cement mortar		
in vertical facing to concrete		
102mm thick	m2	50
215mm thick	m2	80
in columns and piers		
215mm thick	m	15
327mm thick	m	30
440mm thick	m	60
Blockwork; lightweight in cement mortar (1:3), stretcher bond		
in vertical straight walls		
100mm thick	m2	18
140mm thick	m2	25
190mm thick	m2	35
Blockwork; dense in cement mortar (1:3) straight walls		
100mm thick	m2	20

	Unit	£
Blockwork; dense in cement mortar (1:3) straight walls (cont'd)		
140mm thick	m2	25
190mm thick	m2	35
Ashlar masonry, Portland Whitbed with one exposed face in cement lime mortar (1:1:6) in vertical facing to concrete or brickwork		
100mm thick	m2	250
200mm thick	m2	450
Rubble masonry, Cotswold limestone one exposed face, hammer dressed in cement lime mortar (1:1:6)		
200mm thick	m2	60
350mm thick	m2	110
500mm thick	m2	135

CLASS V: PAINTING

(Rates inclusive of all inclinations)

	Unit	£
One coat prime on general surfaces exceeding 300mm		
metal	m2	2
timber	m2	2
Two coats of emulsion paint on general surfaces exceeding 300mm		
smooth concrete	m2	3
blockwork and brickwork	m2	4

	Unit	£
Two coats of cement paint		
smooth concrete	m2	3
blockwork and brickwork	m2	4
rough cast surfaces	m2	5
Three coats of oil paint on		
primed steel sections	m2	7
primed pipework	m2	8
planed timber	m2	7

CLASS W: WATERPROOFING

Damp proofing

	Unit	£
One layer 1000 gauge 'Bituthene' sheet, fixed with adhesive	m2	8
Asphalt to BS1097 two coat work, 10mm thick on concrete surfaces	m2	15

Roofing

	Unit	£
Asphalt to BS908, two coat work, 10mm thick on concrete surfaces	m2	14
Built up felt roofing to BS747, three layer coverings	m2	25

Waterproofing

	Unit	£
Proprietary roof decking with roof felt finish; insulated	m2	35
Protective layers, one layer 1000 gauge polythene sheet, fixed with adhesive	m2	2
Cement and sand (1:3) screed with waterproof-additive	m2	10

Waterproofing (cont'd)	Unit	£
Sprayed or brushed waterproofing two coats of 'Synthaprufe' to concrete surfaces	m2	5

CLASS X: MISCELLANEOUS WORK

Fences

Timber post and rail, driven posts height 1.10m with 4 rails	m	15
Timber round driven posts with 6 wires height 1.00m	m	8
Chain link fencing BS1772, with galvanized mesh, line and tying wire, concrete posts height 1.80m	m	20

Gates

Timber field gates BS3470, 1.10m high

softwood 2.70m wide	nr	200
hardwood 3.30m wide	nr	220

Gate posts 2.30m long

softwood 175 x 175mm	pair	140
concrete 200 x 200mm	pair	220

Drainage to structures above ground

UPVC half round system, to timber with brackets

gutters 110mm	m	7
pipes 68mm	m	8

	Unit	£
Cast iron half round to timber with brackets		
gutters 100mm	m	12
gutters 150mm	m	17
Steel 'Plastisol' coated profiled to timber with over strap joints, 135 x 102mm	m	20

Rock filled gabions

Box type filled with graded broken rock		
size 2000 x 1000 x 1000mm	nr	100
size 4000 x 1000 x 1000mm	nr	175

CLASS Y: SEWER RENOVATION AND ANCILLARY WORKS

Preparation of existing sewers

Cleaning egg shaped sewer 1050mm high	m	9-12
Removing intrusions		
brick	nr	3-5
laterals, clay bore not exceeding 150mm	nr	5-10
Plugging laterals		
bore not exceeding 300mm	nr	25-35
bore 750mm	nr	150-250
Local internal repairs		
areas 0.1-0.25m2	nr	25-35
area 10m2	nr	200-250

	Unit	£
Stabilization of existing sewers		
Pointing with cement mortar (1:3)	m2	15-20
Renovation of existing sewers		
Segmental lining in GRP		
egg shaped 1050mm high	m	200-300
annulus grouting in Pozament	m3	140-180
Laterals to renovated sewers		
Jointing		
bore not exceeding 150mm	nr	25-30
bore 150-300mm	nr	40-45
bore 450mm	nr	60-70
Interruptions		
Preparation of existing sewers		
cleaning	hour	180-220
Stabilization		
pointing	hour	25-35
Renovation		
linings	hour	40-50

CLASS Z: SIMPLE BUILDING WORKS INCIDENTAL TO CIVIL ENGINEERING WORKS

see chapter 3

5

Composite rates

These composite items are mainly an amalgam of different item descriptions and can be used in the quick preparation of approximate quantities. The rates represent the value of the combined scope of the items.

EARTHWORKS

Excavation

General excavation of large area in good conditions	Unit	£
disposal on site up to 500m distance	m3	10
disposal off site up to 10km distance	m3	13
Excavating foundations with JCB in good conditions		
disposal on site up to 500m distance	m3	11
extra for disposal off site up to 10 km distance	m3	14
Cutting for road or railway with scrapers in good conditions	m3	3
Filling and compacting excavated material in layers, large areas	m3	4

	Unit	£

CONCRETE WORK

Pile caps (21N/mm2, 20mm aggregate)

Rates inclusive of excavation, disposal, concrete, formwork, reinforcement at 110 kg per m3 and cutting away top of pile

Excavation 1500mm deep, concrete 1000mm thick

	Unit	£
1000 x 1000mm	nr	300
1500 x 1500mm	nr	500
2000 x 2000mm	nr	900

Excavation 2000mm deep, concrete 1200mm thick

	Unit	£
1000 x 1000mm	nr	400
1500 x 1500mm	nr	700
2000 x 2000mm	nr	1200

Ground beams between pile caps (21N/mm2, 20mm aggregate)

Rates inclusive of excavation, disposal, concrete, formwork and reinforcement at 140 kg per m3

	Unit	£
500 x 500mm deep	m	50
500 x 750mm deep	m	70
600 x 1000mm deep	m	120
750 x 1500mm deep	m	170

	Unit	£
Slabs on fill including blinding, Visqueen and reinforcement at 100kg per m3, thickness		
150mm	m2	35
200mm	m2	40
225mm	m2	45
250mm	m2	50
300mm	m2	60
500mm	m2	90
Extra for waterproof concrete add 10%		
Suspended slabs including formwork and reinforcement at 150kg per m3, thickness		
150mm	m2	50
200mm	m2	60
225mm	m2	70
250mm	m2	75
Beams including formwork and reinforcement at 240kg per m3, size		
250 x 300mm	m	40
300 x 350mm	m	50
350 x 450mm	m	65
450 x 500mm	m	90

Concrete structures (cont'd)	Unit	£
Columns including formwork and reinforcement at 200kg per m3, size		
250 x 250mm	m	25
300 x 300mm	m	35
450 x 500mm	m	70
500 x 500mm	m	80

STRUCTURAL STEELWORK

	Unit	£
Stanchions cased in concrete		
254 x 254 x 132kg/m	m	180
305 x 305 x 240kg/m	m	300
356 x 406 x 467kg/m	m	600
Stanchions cased in 'Supalux' board or similar material		
254 x 254 x 132kg/m	m	175
305 x 305 x 240kg/m	m	290
356 x 406 x 467kg/m	m	580
Beams cased in concrete		
254 x 146 x 43kg/m	m	60
305 x 165 x 54kg/m	m	70
686 x 254 x 152kg/m	m	170
Beams cased in 'Supalux' board or similar material		
254 x 146 x 43kg/m	m	50
305 x 165 x 54kg/m	m	60
686 x 254 x 152kg/m	m	150

BRICKWORK AND BLOCKWORK

These rates are inclusive of forming
openings, cutting, building in ties
and pointing

Thickness of wall

		Half brick £	One brick £	Two brick £
Common brickwork				
vertical straight walls	m2	30	60	95
facing to concrete	m2	33	65	-
casing to steel columns	m2	40	70	-
Facing brickwork				
bricks PC £300/1000				
vertical straight walls	m2	40	80	-
facing to concrete	m2	43	90	-
bricks PC £350/1000				
vertical straight walls	m2	50	100	-
facing to concrete	m2	55	100	-
Engineering brickwork				
bricks £350/1000				
vertical straight walls	m2	45	90	160
piers and columns	m2	-	100	170

		100mm Solid	140mm Solid	215mm Hollow
Dense concrete blockwork				
vertical straight walls	m2	20	25	35
casing to steel columns	m2	24	30	-

	Unit	£
MISCELLANEOUS METAL WORK		
Steelwork staircases 3000 mm rise,		
straight flight 1000mm wide	nr	2500-2800
two flight with half landing	nr	3000-3500
Spiral staircase 2500mm diameter, 3500mm rise	nr	2250-2500
Ladders in steel		
cat ladder; 20mm rungs at 300mm centre, 470mm wide, 3000mm long	nr	500-700
Extra for back hoops	nr	40
ships ladder; 75mm wide treads at 300mm centres, 470mm wide, 3000mm rise	nr	800-1000
Balustrades		
balcony balustrades 835mm high with 15mm balusters at 200mm centres 50 x 15mm rounded handrails	m	70-80
staircase balustrade as above with ramps and wreaths	m	90-100
tubular steel balustrades 835mm high with 40mm diameter standards and handrail, galvanized	m	35-40
Open grid flooring		
50mm galvanized panels	m2	140-160
Durbar plate flooring 8mm thick	m2	90-100

	Unit	£
Plain steel sections, unfabricated beams, built into structure		
457 x 191 x 82kg/m	t	600
356 x 171 x 51kg/m	t	620
254 x 146 x 37kg/m	t	650

DRAINAGE

Pipe laying with allowance for machine excavation, disposal of surplus and fittings

Trenches 1000mm deep, with granular bed and surround

	Unit	£
ductile spun iron 150mm	m	35
vitrified clay 150mm	m	25
uPVC 160mm	m	25

Trenches 1500 mm deep with concrete bed and haunch

	Unit	£
ductile spun iron 250mm	m	50
vitrified clay 225mm	m	40
uPVC 250mm	m	45

Trenches 2000mm deep with concrete bed and surround

	Unit	£
ductile spun iron 450mm	m	114
vitrified clay 400mm	m	95
concrete class H 375mm	m	75

Drainage (cont'd)	Unit	£
Trenches 2500mm deep with granular bed and surround		
vitrified clay 450mm	m	110
concrete class H 450mm	m	80
Trenches 3000mm deep with concrete bed and haunch		
concrete class H 525mm	m	100
Trenches 4000 mm deep with granular bed and haunch		
ductile spun iron 600mm	m	190
concrete class H 750mm	m	135

Agricultural drains ditches and trenches

	Unit	£
Porous stoneware or concrete pipes in trenches not exceeding 0.5m deep		
75mm	m	6
100mm	m	8
150mm	m	10
Trenches excavated and filled with rubble not exceeding 0.5m deep		
rectangular section 0.5m	m	15
vee section ditches unlined not exceeding 0.5m deep	m	10
Trenches for cable ducts (laid by others) average 1000 mm deep		
single way ducts not exceeding 200mm bore	m	6
two way ducts	m	8

	Unit	£

Reinstatement of surfacing

80mm tarmacadam surface with hardcore road base	m	13
150mm concrete surface with hardcore road base	m	25

Manholes

Precast concrete ring manholes with reinforced concrete shaft rings, extra heavy duty concrete cover slab, brickwork shaft and 600 x 600mm heavy duty road manhole cover

	Internal Diameter			
	1350mm £	1500mm £	1800mm £	2100mm £
2000mm deep	800	1000	1200	1400
2500mm deep	950	1150	1350	1600
3000mm deep	1050	1300	1400	1800
3500mm deep	1200	1450	1550	2000

Road gullies

Vitrified clay road gulley 450mm diameter with heavy duty hinged cast iron grating, brickwork raising course	nr	350
Concrete road gulley 450mm diameter and similar grating	nr	150

ROADWORKS

Flexible surfaces

sub base in hardcore; thickness 150mm	m2	3

Roadworks (cont'd)	Unit	£
road base in DTp Type 1; thickness 250mm	m2	7
Dense bitumen macadam 40mm aggregate		
base course 60mm	m2	5
wearing course 40mm	m2	5
Rigid surfaces		
sub base in hardcore 150mm	m2	3
road base in DTp Type 1 200mm	m2	6
concrete surfacing with fabric reinforcement 150mm	m2	15
excavation and disposal 300-500mm	m2	6
average for road construction as above	m2	25
Kerbs and channels		
precast concrete kerbs and foundations including excavation	m	12
precast concrete channels and foundations including excavation	m	15
Tarmacadam road in two layers 80mm thick, 250mm road base on prepared formation including excavation, concrete kerbs each side		
6.0m wide	m	165
7.5m wide	m	190

Project costs

The following information on budget estimating has been extracted from *Cost Information for Water Supply and Sewage Disposal* Technical report TR61 published by the Water Research Centre. The report presents the results of a study, over many years, of costs of projects collected from local authorities and consultants. The results of the studies produced cost functions which can be updated by using indices.

The cost figures used are based on tenders received, not final costs, during the period 1960s to mid 1970s.

It must be emphasized that as with all statistically based, updated information, the results obtained from using the formulae should be treated with caution and the 'confidence limits' applied to the predictions. Reference to the original book will greatly assist the estimator to obtain more accurate results.

There are several sets of indices referred to in this chapter viz: The Construction Index, DQSD Index, Construction Materials Index, and Engineering and Allied Industries Index. If these indices are not readily to hand for updating purposes an indication of the increase from the quoted date may be obtained from the indices given in Chapter 15.

SEWERAGE

$$COST = 0.000717 * LEN^{0.94} * DIAM^{0.72} * DEP^{0.57}$$

	Unit	Min.	Max.
where COST is total cost of scheme,	£'000 1976 Q3	2.5	2,050
LEN is total length of pipework,	m	45	30,000
DIAM is mean diameter of scheme, weighting individual pipe diameters by their lengths,	mm	86	1,440

SEWERAGE (cont'd)

	Unit	Min.	Max.
and DEP is mean depth of scheme, weighting individual pipe depths by their corresponding excavated areas.	m	1.14	7.10

Number of cases: 80

Approximate multipliers for confidence limits about a prediction:

Confidence level	Lower	Upper
80%	0.56	1.78
95%	0.41	2.43

Note   The New Construction Index should be used for inflation (value at 1976 Q3 = 246).

NB. See worked example on page 136.

WATER PUMPING BUILDINGS

$$WATPUMPCOS = 4.00*THRUPUT^{0.79}$$

	Unit	Min.	Max.
where WATPUMPCOS is total construction cost	£'000 1976 Q3	49.2	874
and THRUPUT is design throughput.	'000 m3/d	15	680

Number of cases: 11

Approximate multipliers for confidence limits about a prediction:

Confidence level	Lower	Upper
80%	0.49	2.06
95%	0.31	3.26

Note: 1. The DQSD Index should be used for inflation (value at 1976 Q3 = 246).

NB. See worked example on page 137.

WATER MAINS

$$COST = 0.0702*LEN^{0.73}*DIAM^{0.91}(DIAM/(1000 + DIAM))$$

	Unit	Min.	Max.
where COST is total cost of scheme,	£'000 1976 Q3	70.3	2,050
LEN is total length of pipework,	m	70.3	4,770
DIAM is mean diameter of scheme, weighting individual pipe diameters by their lengths,	m	744	45,500
and DEP is mean depth of scheme, weighting individual pipe depths by their corresponding excavated areas.	mm	126	1,830

Number of cases: 37

Approximate multipliers for confidence limits about a prediction:

Confidence level	Lower	Upper
80%	0.64	1.55
95%	0.51	1.98

Note: 1. The New Construction Index should be used for inflation (value at 1976 Q3 = 246).

TUNNELS AND SHAFTS

$$COST = 0.0265 * VOL^{1.07}$$

	Unit	Min.	Max.
where COST is total tunnels and shafts cost of a scheme(see Note 2 below),	£million 1976 Q3	0.148	4.23
and VOL is the sum of the excavated volumes of the individual tunnels and shafts making up the contract.	'000m3	4.75	131

Number of cases: 9

Approximate multipliers for confidence limits about a prediction:

Confidence level	Lower	Upper
80%	0.76	1.31
95%	0.64	1.57

Note: 1. The Construction Materials Index should be used for inflation (value at 1976 Q3 = 258).

2. COST is the cost of the individual tunnels and shafts making up the contract (assuming wedge-blocked lining), but excluding costs of secondary lining, shafts fittings, internal pipes and general and preliminary items.

3. Total contract cost may be estimated by first applying the above model and then multiplying by a LINING factor, which takes the value 1.43 for wedge-block lining, 1.57 for bolted concrete segment lining, and 2.00 for cast iron segment lining. This procedure is discussed more fully in Section 10.3D.

INTAKES

Intake stations should be considered as pumping stations (with or without pumping plant) together with the additional bankside civil engineering and screening plant costs. Both of these additional items depend largely upon circumstances, but making simplifying assumptions the following table can be constructed.

£'000 1976 Q3

| Throughput ('000 m3/d) | Pumping station | | Intake station |
	Building	Building and Pumping plant	Pumping station with intake structure and plant
2	6.92	13.5	19.6
5	14.3	27.6	41.4
10	24.7	47.4	69.8
20	42.6	81.4	120
50	88.0	167	230
100	152	286	382
200	263	491	640
500	542	1000	1310

Note: 1. The multipliers for confidence intervals about a prediction have been assumed to be similar to those given for the water pumping station building and pumping plant models; approximate values are as follows:

Confidence level	Lower	Upper
80%	0.5	2.0
95%	0.33	3.0

2. The New Construction Index should be used for inflation of civil engineering items (value at 1976 Q3 = 263).

INTAKES (cont'd)

3. The Engineering and Allied Industries Index should be used for inflation of plant items (value at 1976 Q3 = 227).

4. The figures assume a 50% standby pumping plant capacity.

5. Costs exclude any major interconnecting aqueduct between the intake and the pumping station.

SEWAGE PUMPING BUILDINGS

$$SEWCOS = 1.63*CAP^{0.29}*HEAD^{0.19}*NPUMP^{0.89}$$

	Unit	Min.	Max.
where SEWCOS is total plant cost,	£'000 1976 Q3	2.74	96.0
CAP is total installed capacity (see Note 2 below),	1/s	1	1350
HEAD is total head,	m	1.5	60.9
and NPUMP is number of pumps installed.	-	1	7

Number of cases: 58

Approximate multipliers for confidence limits about a prediction:

Confidence level	Lower	Upper
80%	0.59	1.68
95%	0.45	2.23

Note: 1. The Engineering and Allied Industries Index should be used for inflation (value at 1976 Q3 = 227)

2. CAP is the combined operating and standby capacity (the extent of standby is decided by the user).

SEWAGE PUMPING BUILDINGS

$$COST = 6.97*DESCAP^{0.21}*DESNPUMP^{0.60}$$

	Unit	Min.	Max.
where PUMPCOS is total construction cost,	£'000 1976 Q3	6.68	130
DESCAP is design capacity,	1/s	2	1440
and DESNPUMP is design number of pumps.	-	1	7

Number of cases: 58

Approximate multipliers for confidence limits about a prediction:

Confidence level	Lower	Upper
80%	0.58	1.74
95%	0.43	2.34

Note: 1. The New Construction Index should be used for inflation (value at 1976 Q3 = 263).

2. To estimate the cost of a complete pumping station, this digest should be used in conjunction with the sewerage pumping plant digest.

NB. See worked example on page 137.

CONCRETE DAMS

$$CONCOS = 0.0569*DAMVOL^{0.95}$$

	Unit	Min.	Max.
where CONCOS is total cost of dam (see Note 2 below),	£ million 1976 Q3	1.13	12.1

CONCRETE DAMS (cont'd)

and DAMVOL is volume of fill
of dam.   '000m3   19,252

Number of cases: 13

Approximate multipliers for confidence limits about a prediction:

Confidence level	Lower	Upper
80%	0.77	1.29
95%	0.71	1.40

Note: 1. The Construction Materials Index should be used for
inflation (value at 1976 Q3 = 258).

2. CONCOS includes the cost of the dam, cut-off, adjacent or
integral inlet and outlet works, integral pipe and tunnel
works, and minor diversions and ancillary works.

NB. See worked example on page 137-8.

EARTHBANK DAMS (with concrete cut-off walls)

$$CONWALLCOS = 8.97*DAMVOL^{0.66}$$

	Unit	Min.	Max.
where CONWALLCOS is total cost of dam (see Note 3 below),	£ million 1976 Q3	2.61	18.9
and DAMVOL is volume of fill of dam, including all material placed and compacted.	million m3	0.116	3.00

Number of cases: 10

Approximate multipliers for confidence limits about a prediction:

Confidence level	Lower	Upper
80%	0.81	1.24
95%	0.70	1.42

Note: 1. The Construction Materials Index should be used for inflation (value at 1976 Q3 = 258).

2. The function applies only to earthbank dams constructed with a concrete cut-off wall that is substantial enough to act also as the core.

3. CONWALLCOS includes the cost of the dam, cut-off, adjacent or integral inlet and outlet works, integral pipe and tunnel works, and minor diversions and ancillary works.

EARTHBANK DAMS (with clay cores)

$$CLAYCORECOS = 4.53*DAMVOL^{0.73}*TYPE^{-0.58}$$

	Unit	Min.	Max.
where CLAYCORECOS is total cost of dam (see Note 3 below),	£ million 1976 Q3	1.07	11.9
and DAMVOL is volume of fill of dam, including all material placed and compacted.	million m3	0.195	7.65

and TYPE is 2 for clay-cored bunds and 1 for other clay-cored dams.

Number of cases: 22

Approximate multipliers for confidence limits about a prediction:

Confidence level	Lower	Upper
80%	0.82	1.22
95%	0.73	1.36

Note: 1. The Construction Materials Index should be used for inflation (value at 1976 Q3 = 258).

2. The effect on cost of using some rockfill or concrete grouting was statistically insignificant.

EARTHBANK DAMS (cont'd)

3. CLAYCORECOS includes the cost of the dam, cut-off, adjacent or integral inlet and outlet works, integral pipe and tunnel works, and minor diversions and ancillary works.

NB. See worked example on page 138.

RESERVOIRS AND LAGOONS

$$CLAYBUNCOS = 1.05*RESVOL^{0.68}$$

	Unit	Min.	Max.
where CLAYBUNCOS is total cost of embankment Note 3 below),	£ million 1976 Q3	0.0135	11.9
and RESVOL is the storage volume.	million m3	0.00226	37.7

Number of cases: 13

Approximate multipliers for confidence limits about a prediction:

Confidence level	Lower	Upper
80%	0.82	1.22
95%	0.73	1.36

Note: 1. The Construction Materials Index should be used for inflation (value at 1976 Q3 = 258).

2. The function applies only to clay-cored totally bunded reservoirs and simple excavated and/or bunded lagoons.

3. CLAYBUNCOS includes the cost of the dam, cut-off, adjacent or integral inlet and outlet works, integral pipe and tunnel works, and minor diversions and ancillary works.

WHOLE WATER TREATMENT WORKS

Total capital cost of water treatment works (£'000 1976 Q3)

Throughput ('000 m3/d)	Rock and moorland raw water Type (iii)		Moorland raw water Type (iv)	Lowland raw water Type (v)
	Pressure filtration	Gravity filtration	Sedimentation-filtration	
2	233	259	-	-
5	408	441	585	599
10	614	673	924	917
20	915	1,040	1,460	1,410
50	1,700	1,880	2,680	2,440
100	2,800	3,120	4,210	3,970
200	-	4,890	6,910	6,220
500	-	9,610	13,200	12,000

Confidence level	Approximate multipliers for confidence limits about a prediction			
80% (Upper	1.33	1.23	1.17	1.17
(Lower	0.75	0.81	0.85	0.85
95% (Upper	1.56	1.37	1.28	1.28
(Lower	0.64	0.72	0.78	0.78

Note: 1. Although no single index is appropriate for all the water treatment cost components, the New Construction Index was chosen in more than half the cases and so could reasonably be used here for inflation (value at 1976 Q3 = 263).

2. Cost includes civil engineering and building costs, mechanical and electrical engineering costs and sludge process costs, and includes all costs relating to conditions of contract. Costs associated with additional processes (see Section 12.6) and extra items (see Section 12.8.3) are excluded.

3. Costs have not been estimated separately for treatment of groundwater (raw water Type i) or upland rock water (raw water Type ii).

SERVICE RESERVOIRS

$$COST = 0.0636*CAP^{0.64}$$

	Unit	Min.	Max.
where COST is total cost of (rectangular concrete-covered) service reservoir,	1976 Q3		
and CAP is tank capacity.	'000 m3	0.340	114

Number of cases: 47

Approximate multipliers for confidence limits about a prediction:

Confidence level	Lower	Upper
80%	0.69	1.44
95%	0.57	1.76

Note: 1. The New Construction Index should be used for inflation (value at 1976 Q3 = 263).

WATER TOWERS

$$COST = 162*CAP^{0.77}*TYPE^{-0.56}$$

	Unit	Min.	Max.
where COST is total cost,	£'000 1976 Q3	11.5	514
and CAP is tank capacity,	'000 m3	0.060	3.41
and TYPE is 1 for concrete water towers, and 2 for steel water towers.			

Number of cases: 21

Approximate multipliers for confidence limits about a prediction:

Confidence level	Lower	Upper
80%	0.70	1.43
95%	0.57	1.77

Note: 1. The New Construction Index should be used for inflation (value at 1976 Q3 = 263).

2. The overall height of tower was not a significant variable; this is probably because of the limited variation of heights within the sample. The mean sample height was 25.1 m.

WHOLE SEWAGE TREATMENT WORKS

River and estuarine discharge

Capital costs (£'000 1976 Q3)

Dry weather flow ('000 m3/d)		River				Estuarine	
	Effluent standard (SS/BOD/ammoniacal nitrogen)						
	10/10/10		30/20		150/200		
	Civil	Mech.	Civil	Mech.	Civil	Mech.
2.5	522	229	452	184	-	-
5	947	377	753	303	371	169
10	1060	563	889	391	588	328
20	1710	944	1410	654	838	350
40	2760	1430	2250	937	1410	604
80	4820	2620	3950	1780	2370	931
160	7960	4210	6480	2770	3880	1650

Confidence level   Approximate multipliers for confidence limits about a prediction

80%						
(Upper	1.12	1.19	1.12	1.19	1.14	1.20
(Lower	0.89	0.84	0.89	0.84	0.88	0.83
95%						
(Upper	1.18	1.30	1.18	1.30	1.21	1.32
(Lower	0.85	0.77	0.85	0.77	0.83	0.76

WHOLE SEWAGE TREATMENT WORKS (cont'd)

Note: 1. The civil engineering and the mechanical engineering costs have both been presented so that cost predictions can be corrected for inflation. The New Construction Index should be used for inflation of the civil engineering costs (value at 1976 Q3 = 263); for the mechanical engineering costs the Engineering and Allied Industries Index should be used (value at 1976 Q3 = 227).

2. The costs include sludge process costs and all costs relating to conditions of contract. Costs associated with contractors' overheads, optional equipment such as administrative and laboratory buildings, and work specific to the site such as access roads, are excluded.

NB. See worked example on page 138-9.

Examples

The following demonstrates the use of some of the formulae to calculate various budget estimates.

1. Sewage scheme

$$COST = 0.000717*LEN^{0.94}*DIAM^{0.72}*DEP^{0.57}$$

Assume the scheme has the following pipes

1. 1500m 500mm pipes
2. 750m   300mm pipes
3. 500m   225mm pipes
4. 500m   150mm pipes
5. 1000m 100mm pipes

LEN 4250m 0.94 = 2574
DIAM 225mm 0.72 = 49
DEP 210m 0.57 = 15
From the formula cost = 0.000717 x 2574 x 49 x 1.5 = 135.65 x 100

Total construction cost = £135,650 3Q 1976 Base date
                        = £474,770 1Q 1990 Estimate date

80% confidence level £265,871 - £845,090

2. Water pumping building

$$COST = 4.00 * THRUPUT^{0.79}$$

Assume design throughput 45,000 m3/day
From formula
Total construction cost = £4 x 45$^{0.79}$

$$= 80.928$$

say £81,000 at 3Q 1976

£292,150 at 1Q 1990

3. Sewage pumping building

$$PUMPCOST = 6.97*DESCAP^{0.21}*DESNPUMP^{0.60}$$

PUMPCOST = total construction cost 000's

DESCAP = design capacity

DESNPUMP = design number of pumps

Assume design capacity = 300 l/s

number of pumps = 3

From formula

Total construction cost = $6.97 \times 300^{0.21} \times 3^{0.60}$

$$= 6.97 \times 3.31 \times 1.93$$

$$= 40.42$$

$$= £40,420 \text{ at 3Q 1976}$$

$$= £145,926 \text{ at 1Q 1990}$$

4. Concrete dam

$$COST = 0.569*VOL^{0.95}$$

Assume the volume of the dam 150,000 m3

From the formula : VOL in 000's

Concrete dams (cont'd)

Total construction cost $= 0.0569 \times 150^{0.95}$

$= 0.0569 \times 116.76$

$= £6.64$ million in 3Q 1976

$= £23.98$ in 1Q 1990

Say   £24 million

5. Earthbank dam (Clay-cored bund)

$COST = 4.53 * VOL^{0.73} * TYPE^{-0.58}$

Assume the volume of the dam 150,000m3

From the formula : VOL in 000's

Total construction cost $= 4.53 \times 0.15^{0.73} \times 2^{-0.58}$

$= 4.53 \times 0.25 \times 0.67$

$= 0.76$

$= £758,775$ at 3Q 1976

$= £2,739,178$ at 1Q 1990

6. Whole sewage treatment works

For the purpose of calculating a 'global cost' for a whole sewage treatment works some basic criteria are required to be known.

1) Dry weather flow in '000 m3/d

2) Effluent standard (SS/BOD/ammoniacal nitrogen)

3) River or Estuarine discharge

From the table:-

Assuming : 10,000m3 per day
            30/20 Standard
            River discharge

From the table : Civil Costs   £889,000
                Mechanical Costs   £391,000
                                    £1,280,000 at 1976 3Q

            Probable cost   £4,500,000 at 1990 1Q

    80% Confidence level   £5,000,000 - £3,900,000

Part Three

Mechanical and Electrical Work

The square metre rates given for the mechanical and electrical work are for typical buildings. The rates assume that all public services are available on site. Professional fees are also excluded.

The rates are to be applied to the total floor area of all storeys of the building. The area measured is that between the external walls without deduction for internal walls or staircases.

Ranges of prices given for each building are typical. Specific requirements of the building(s) being considered must be taken into account. If varying types of buildings are used on a project as a whole, then the rates may need to be adjusted to allow for common preliminaries, site set-up, administration costs, plant etc.

The prices do not include incidental builders' work, profit and attendance or 2½% cash discount for the main contractor.

Payments to statutory authorities and public undertakings for service provision or work carried out by them have been excluded.

The headings A, B and C given, classify the buildings into:

A - Speculative

B - Purpose Built - Class 1

C - Purpose Built - Class 2

Within the purpose built heading, Class 1 relates to those buildings that the Owner/Developer dictates specific requirements but where the engineering content is of an average complexity. For Class 2, the building is also purpose built but the engineering content is above average complexity. Where rates are not included it is considered that this class is not applicable.

The rates do not allow for machinery, computer terminals, kitchen and laundry equipment, sanitary ware, sprinkler systems and the like.

MECHANICAL INSTALLATION

£ per square metre

Industrial	A	B	C
Factories	15-35	20-40	40-55
Warehousing	14-28	18-35	-
Assembly and machine workshops	-	40-50	50-68
Garage/showrooms	-	20-40	-
Transport garages	-	20-30	-
Agricultural			
Barns, sheds, glass houses	-	5-10	-
Animal breeding units	-	15-20	-
Commercial			
Shops	45-65	50-75	-
Offices	55-95	130-180	180-250
Hotels	-	70-100	115-170
Supermarkets	-	120-170	-
Department stores	-	130-170	-
Telecommunications	-	160-190	210-250
Computer installations	-	160-200	200-240
Community			
Community centres	-	80-120	-
Ambulance and fire stations	-	110-160	-
Bus stations	-	30-50	60-110

	£ per square metre		
	A	B	C
Police stations	-	120-170	-
Prisons	-	-	150-200
Churches	-	60-90	-
Concert halls/theatres	-	110-140	150-200
Museums/libraries/ art galleries	-	110-150	150-190
Magistrates/county courts	-	200-250	-
Crown/high courts	-	-	250-280
Residential			
Dormitory hostels	-	50-60	-
Estate/sheltered housing	-	30-40	-
Houses for individuals	18-22	18-32	32-40
Education			
Middle/secondary schools	-	70-100	-
University buildings			
Administration	-	80-100	-
Laboratory/research	-	90-160	-
Halls of residence	-	50-70	-
Recreation			
Sports centres	-	80-100	-
Squash courts	-	40-60	-
Swimming pools	-	80-100	-

	£ per square metre		
Medical Services	A	B	C
Clinics and health centres	-	90-120	-
Homes for the elderly	-	60-80	-
Disabled accommodation	-	60-80	-
G.P. surgeries	-	40-50	-
Dental surgeries	-	40-50	-
General hospitals	-	-	200-300
Teaching hospitals	-	-	200-300
Hospital laboratories	-	100-180	180-350

ELECTRICAL INSTALLATION

Industrial

	A	B	C
Factories	20-30	25-35	35-55
Warehousing	15-30	25-40	-
Assembly and machine workshops	-	35-40	50-70
Garages/showrooms	-	12-28	-
Transport garages	-	14-25	-

Agricultural

	A	B	C
Barns, sheds, glass houses	-	5-10	-
Animal breeding units	-	15-25	-

Commercial

	A	B	C
Shops	30-45	40-50	-
Offices	60-80	90-150	150-180

	£ per square metre		
	A	B	C
Hotels	-	50-80	90-150
Supermarkets	-	80-120	-
Departmental stores	-	80-130	-
Telecommunications	-	100-160	160-180
Computer installations	-	100-160	160-200
Community			
Community centres	-	60-80	-
Ambulance and fire stations	-	90-130	-
Bus stations	-	30-40	40-50
Police stations	-	100-140	-
Prisons	-	-	80-120
Churches	-	15-20	-
Concert halls/theatres	-	100-120	120-140
Museums/libraries/ art galleries	-	60-90	90-120
Magistrates/county courts	-	70-120	-
Crown/high courts	-	-	120-180
Residential			
Dormitory hostels	-	25-40	-
Estate/sheltered housing	-	25-35	-
Houses for individuals	15-30	15-30	20-35

Education	£ per square metre		
	A	B	C
Middle/secondary schools	-	45-60	-
University buildings			
Administration	-	55-70	-
Laboratory/research	-	60-80	-
Halls of residence	-	30-40	-
Recreation			
Sports centres	-	25-30	-
Squash courts	-	20-25	-
Swimming pools	-	25-30	-
Medical services			
Clinics and health centres	-	25-40	-
Homes for the elderly	-	20-30	-
Disabled accommodation	-	20-40	-
General practice surgeries	-	20-30	-
Dental surgeries	-	20-30	-
General hospitals	-	-	100-140
Teaching hospitals	-	-	100-140
Hospital laboratories	-	60-90	90-110

MECHANICAL INSTALLATION BASIC SERVICES

Industrial	£ per square metre		
	A	B	C
Factories, assembly and machine workshops			
Heating and ventilation	19.00	25.00	35.00
Compressed air installation	10.00	18.00	22.00
Water services	5.00	5.00	5.00
Fire protection	3.00	3.00	3.00
(Process steam and ventilation are excluded)			
Agricultural			
Heating and ventilation	-	2.00	5.00
Water services	-	2.00	4.00
Shops/Stores			
Heating and ventilation	40.00	-	-
Air conditioning	-	110.00	-
Water services	4.00	4.00	-
Fire protection	4.00	4.00	-
Offices			
Heating and ventilation	50.00	-	-
Air conditioning	-	100.00	130.00
Water services	10.00	11.00	12.00
Fire protection	4.00	4.00	4.00

Telecommunications/computer installation

	£ per square metre		
	A	B	C
Heating and ventilation	-	25.00	30.00
Air conditioning	-	120.00	140.00
Water services	-	8.00	10.00
Fire protection	-	4.00	4.00

Community

Heating and ventilation	-	40.00	50.00
Air conditioning	-	160.00	190.00
Water services	-	10.00	12.00
Fire protection	-	4.00	5.00

Residential

Heating and ventilation	20.00	25.00	30.00
Water services	8.00	10.00	12.00

Education

Heating	-	40.00	60.00
Ventilation	-	15.00	35.00
Water services	-	20.00	30.00
Fire protection	-	4.00	4.00

Recreation

Heating	-	15.00	20.00
Ventilation	-	5.00	7.00
Air conditioning	-	22.00	30.00

	A	B	C
		£ per square metre	
Water services	-	25.00	35.00
Fire protection	-	4.00	4.00

Medical services

	A	B	C
Heating	-	50.00	60.00
Ventilation	-	40.00	70.00
Air conditioning	-	50.00	140.00
Water services	-	20.00	40.00
Fire protection	-	10.00	10.00

(Medical gases, vacuum
and other dedicated
services are excluded).

ELECTRICAL INSTALLATIONS BASIC SERVICES

Industrial

Factories, assembly and machine workshops	£ per square metre		
	A	B	C
Mains power and switch gear (excludes production supplies)	8.00	9.00	10.00
Telephones	1.00	1.00	1.20
General lighting including fittings	15.00	17.00	20.00
Emergency lighting	3.00	4.00	4.00
Fire protection	2.00	3.00	4.00
Communications	1.00	1.00	1.20

Agricultural	£ per square metre		
	A	B	C
Mains power and switch gear	-	2.00	3.00
Lighting including fittings	-	3.00	4.00

COMMERCIAL

Shops/stores

	A	B	C
Mains power and switch gear	14.00	20.00	-
General lighting including fittings	20.00	40.00	-
Emergency lighting	4.00	5.00	-
Telephones	1.00	1.25	-
External lighting	-	1.00	-
Public address	-	1.00	-
Security	-	4.00	-
Fire protection	5.00	5.00	-
Lightning protection	1.10	1.10	-

Offices

	A	B	C
Mains power and switch gear	36.00	45.00	60.00
General lighting including fittings	30.00	35.00	45.00
Emergency lighting	4.00	6.00	8.00
Telephones	1.00	1.00	2.00
External lighting	0.50	1.00	1.50

		£ per square metre	
	A	B	C
Public address	-	1.10	1.30
Security	-	4.00	5.00
Fire protection	5.00	5.00	5.00
Lightning protection	1.10	1.10	1.10

Telecommunications/computer installation

	A	B	C
Mains power and switch gear	-	60.00	80.00
General lighting including fittings	-	45.00	60.00
Emergency lighting	-	6.00	8.00
Telephones	-	1.00	3.00
Security	-	4.00	5.00
Fire protection	-	5.00	5.00
Lightning protection	-	1.10	1.10

Community

	A	B	C
Mains power and switch gear	-	36.00	45.00
General lighting including fittings	-	30.00	50.00
Emergency lighting	-	4.00	5.00
Telephones	-	1.00	2.00
Security	-	2.00	3.00
Fire protection	-	5.00	5.00

Community (cont'd)	£ per square metre		
	A	B	C
External lighting	-	1.00	1.50
Lightning protection	-	1.10	1.10
Residential			
Mains power and switch gear	12.00	13.00	14.00
Lighting (including fittings)	8.00	9.00	10.00
Security	-	4.00	5.00
Telephones	-	1.40	1.60
Education			
Mains power and switch gear	-	18.00	20.00
General lighting including fittings	-	22.00	25.00
Emergency lighting	-	4.00	5.00
Telephones	-	1.00	1.20
Security	-	2.00	3.00
Fire protection	-	5.00	5.00
External lighting	-	1.00	1.50
Recreation			
Mains power and switch gear	-	12.00	-
General lighting including fittings	-	18.00	-
Emergency lighting	-	4.00	-

	£ per square metre		
	A	B	C
Telephones	-	1.00	-
Security	-	1.10	-
Fire protection	-	5.00	-
External lighting	-	1.00	-
Medical services			
Mains power and switch gear	-	18.00	26.00
General lighting including fittings	-	20.00	26.00
Emergency lighting	-	4.00	5.00
Telephones	-	1.00	1.20
Security	-	1.20	1.50
Fire protection	-	5.00	5.00
Lightning protection	-	1.10	1.10

The rates given for the mechanical and electrical services are for typical installations using average numbers of fittings and joints in relation to straight runs of pipework, conduit, trays, or trunking. For example, in the case of an office block with structural columns projecting in from the external wall and with a low temperature hot water system and dado height trunking, the linear metre rates do not allow for all the additional bends or sets around the columns. The figures in this particular case would need to be adjusted.

Where ranges of prices are given, the specific requirements of the installation or plant items must be taken into account. Adjustments will also need to be made for the size of project undertaken. For example with a very small project the overheads will be greater in proportion to the pipe or conduit length installed than in the case of a larger project.

The rates for plant and equipment include for normal works testing, delivery to site, off loading, storage, distribution up to 100 metres, and installation costs. The rates do not allow for any associated scaffolding or the use of tressels during the installation nor for any associated builder's work, profit and attendance or 2½% cash discount for the Main Contractor.

MECHANICAL WORK

Distribution pipework outside plant rooms

Mild steel pipework

Mild steel tube to BS1387 with joints as listed with normal allowance for fittings, brackets (clips directly to pipework) and wastage. Rates assume average runs. Thermal insulation is priced elsewhere. Valves not included in the rates.

Screwed jointing and fittings, nominal diameter		Heavy Weight £		Medium Weight £
15mm	m	36.00	m	33.00
20mm	m	19.00	m	18.00
25mm	m	20.00	m	19.00
32mm	m	21.00	m	20.00

Screwed jointing and fittings, nominal diameter		Heavy Weight £		Medium Weight £
40mm	m	22.00	m	21.00
50mm	m	44.00	m	42.00
65mm	m	53.00	m	46.00
80mm	m	58.00	m	54.00
100mm	m	60.00	m	58.00
125mm	m	68.00	m	64.00
150mm	m	115.00	m	110.00

Extra over for malleable iron fittings to BS143, nominal diameter		Elbow £		Tee £
15mm	nr	8.00	nr	12.00
20mm	nr	11.00	nr	15.00
25mm	nr	13.00	nr	18.00
32mm	nr	15.00	nr	21.00
40mm	nr	17.00	nr	24.00
50mm	nr	21.00	nr	30.00
65mm	nr	28.00	nr	40.00
80mm	nr	34.00	nr	45.00
100mm	nr	50.00	nr	65.00
125mm	nr	78.00	nr	112.00
150mm	nr	112.00	nr	155.00

Weld jointing and fittings, nominal diameter		Heavy Weight £		Medium Weight £
15mm	m	19.00	m	17.00
20mm	m	22.00	m	21.00
25mm	m	25.00	m	22.00
32mm	m	26.00	m	23.00
40mm	m	27.00	m	24.00
50mm	m	55.00	m	52.00
65mm	m	68.00	m	60.00
80mm	m	72.00	m	62.00
100mm	m	80.00	m	70.00
125mm	m	98.00	m	85.00
150mm	m	115.00	m	98.00

Extra over for heavy weight weldable fittings to BS1965 including welded joints, nominal diameter	Elbow Long Radius 90° £		Tee Equal £	
25mm	nr	15.00	nr	30.00
32mm	nr	18.00	nr	34.00
40mm	nr	20.00	nr	38.00
50mm	nr	27.00	nr	50.00
65mm	nr	36.00	nr	65.00
80mm	nr	45.00	nr	73.00
100mm	nr	56.00	nr	95.00
125mm	nr	75.00	nr	150.00
150mm	nr	93.00	nr	176.00

N.B. for sizes 15mm and 20mm assumed pulled bends with branch welds in lieu of tees.

Copper pipework

Light gauge copper tube to BS2871 Part 1 Table X with joints as listed, with normal allowance for fittings, brackets (clips to insulation spaces for cold water services, clips to pipe for hot water services) and wastage. Rates assume average runs. Thermal insulation priced elsewhere. Valves not included in the measure.

Soft solder capillary joints, nominal diameter	CWS £		HWS £	
15mm	m	16.00	m	15.00
22mm	m	18.00	m	16.00
28mm	m	20.00	m	18.00
35mm	m	23.00	m	21.00
42mm	m	32.00	m	30.00
54mm	m	34.00	m	32.00

Extra over for capillary fittings to BS864, nominal diameter	Coupling £		Elbow £		Tee £	
15mm	nr	4.00	nr	4.00	nr	6.00
22mm	nr	5.00	nr	5.00	nr	7.00
28mm	nr	6.00	nr	6.00	nr	8.00
35mm	nr	7.00	nr	8.00	nr	13.00
42mm	nr	8.00	nr	10.00	nr	16.00
54mm	nr	10.00	nr	16.00	nr	23.00

Copper pipework (cont'd)		CWS £		HWS £
Manipulative compression joints, nominal diameter				
15mm	m	15.00	m	13.00
22mm	m	16.00	m	14.00
28mm	m	20.00	m	18.00
35mm	m	23.00	m	22.00
42mm	m	33.00	m	32.00
54mm	m	38.00	m	36.00

Extra over for compression fittings to BS864, nominal diameter

	Coupling £		Elbow £		Tee £
15mm	nr 4.00	nr	4.00	nr	5.00
22mm	nr 5.00	nr	5.00	nr	7.00
28mm	nr 6.00	nr	7.00	nr	10.00
35mm	nr 9.00	nr	10.00	nr	15.00
42mm	nr 11.00	nr	14.00	nr	21.00
54mm	nr 15.00	nr	21.00	nr	30.00

Bronze welded jointing, nominal diameter		CWS £		HWS £
67mm	m	98.00	m	95.00

Extra over for bronze welded fittings, nominal diameter

	Coupling £		Elbow £		Tee £
54mm	nr 15.00	nr	20.00	nr	30.00

Thermal insulation

Pipework

Pre-formed, rigid section mineral fibre sections, thickness as indicated, with foil faced finish, fixed with adhesive and aluminium bands at 300mm centres. All joints and ends vapour sealed, including all pipe fittings, flanges and valves, mitred bends and tees.

Nominal diameter		Thickness of insulation		
		25mm		40mm
		£		£
15mm	m	10.00	m	11.00
20mm	m	11.00	m	12.00
25mm	m	12.00	m	13.00
32mm	m	13.00	m	14.00
40mm	m	14.00	m	15.00
50mm	m	15.00	m	16.00
65mm	m	16.00	m	17.00
80mm	m	19.00	m	20.00
100mm	m	21.00	m	22.00
125mm	m	26.00	m	27.00
150mm	m	28.00	m	30.00

Pre-formed, rigid section mineral fibre sections, thickness as indicated, with scrim canvas finish, fixed with aluminium bands at 500mm centres, with 0.6mm thick aluminium sheet secured with rivets or self tapping screws, including all pipe fittings, flanges and valves, mitred bends and tees.

Nominal diameter		Thickness of insulation		
		25mm		40mm
		£		£
15mm	m	20.00	m	23.00
20mm	m	21.00	m	24.00
25mm	m	22.00	m	25.00
32mm	m	23.00	m	26.00
40mm	m	24.00	m	27.00
50mm	m	28.00	m	33.00
65mm	m	32.00	m	38.00
80mm	m	40.00	m	45.00
100mm	m	44.00	m	50.00
125mm	m	50.00	m	55.00
150mm	m	55.00	m	65.00

Ductwork and flat surfaces

Mineral fibre rigid slab reinforced aluminium foil faced, fixed to ductwork with pins and adhesive, joints and ends sealed with adhesive tape.

Thickness of insulation	Surface Area Covered	
		£
25mm	m2	15.00
40mm	m2	16.00
50mm	m2	17.00

Ductwork and flat surfaces (cont'd)	Surface Area Covered £
Extra for 0.9mm thick hammer clad aluminium sheet secured with rivets and self tapping screws	m2 18.00

Mineral fibre mattress, reinforced, foil faced, fixed to ductwork with pins and adhesive, and secured with 25mm galvanized wire mesh netting, joints and ends sealed with self-adhesive tape.

Thickness of insulation	Surface Area Covered £
25mm	m2 10.00
40mm	m2 11.00
50mm	m2 12.00

Boilers

Gas-fired, low temperature hot water heating boiler plant of shell and tube construction comprising of:

   2 nr boilers each rated at 60% heating load capacity, complete with boiler mountings and instruments
   1 nr shunt pump
   2 nr variable temperature circulating pumps
   1 nr 3-port valve arrangement for compensated circuit
   2 nr constant temperature circulating pumps
   Boiler control panel
   Field located automatic controls
   Feed and expansion tank
   2 nr twin walled, stainless steel flues and all necessary distribution pipework, fittings, valves, thermal insulation, open vent and cold feed, including delivery, setting to work and commissioning.

Installed boiler capacity	Total cost
300kw	£40,000-55,000
1000kw	£55,000-70,000

Extra for pressurization equipment in lieu of feed and expansion tank, cold feed and open vent.

300kw	£5,000
1000kw	£7,000

Gas-fired, low temperature hot water heating boiler plant of shell and tube construction, comprising of:

2 nr boilers, each rated at 60% heating load capacity complete with boiler mountings and instruments
2 nr copper storage calorifiers
1 nr shunt pump
2 nr variable temperature circulating pumps
1 nr 3-port valve arrangement for compensated circuit
2 nr constant temperature circulating pumps
2 nr hot water service circulating pumps
boiler control panel
field located automatic controls
feed and expansion tank
2 nr twin walled, stainless steel flues and all necessary distribution pipework, fittings, valves, thermal insulation, open vent and cold feed, including delivery, setting to work and commissioning.

Installed boiler capacity	Total cost
300kw	£40,000-60,000
1000kw	£60,000-80,000

Extra for pressurization equipment in lieu of feed and expansion tank, cold feed and open vent for both LTHW and HWS systems.

300kw	£10,000
1000kw	£11,000

Oil-fired, using 35 sec oil, low temperature hot water heating boiler plant of shell and tube construction comprising of:

2 nr boilers each rated at 60% heating load capacity complete with boiler mountings and instruments
2 nr oil storage tanks, gravity supply
1 nr shunt pump
2 nr variable temperature circulating pumps
1 nr 3-port valve arrangement for compensated circuit
2 nr constant temperature circulating pumps
boiler control panel including back end protection
field located automatic controls
feed and expansion tank
2 nr twin walled, stainless steel flues and all necessary distribution pipework, fittings, valves, thermal insulation, open vent and cold feed, including delivery, setting to work and commissioning.

Installed boiler capacity	Total cost
300kw	£40,000-60,000
1000kw	£60,000-80,000

Extra for pressurization equipment in lieu of feed and expansion tank cold feed and open vent.

300kw	£5,000
1000kw	£7,000

Oil-fired, using 35 sec oil, low temperature hot water heating boiler plant of shell and tube construction, comprising of:

2 nr boilers each rated at 60% heating load capacity complete with boiler mountings and intruments
2 nr oil storage tanks, gravity supply
2 nr copper storage calorifiers
1 nr shunt pump
2 nr variable temperature circulating pumps
1 nr 3-port valve arrangement for compensated circuit
2 nr constant temperature circulating pumps
2 nr hot water service circulating pumps
boiler control panel
field located automatic controls
feed and expansion tank
2 nr twin walled, stainless steel flues and all necessary distribution pipework, fittings, valves, thermal insulation, open vent and cold feed, including delivery, setting to work and commissioning

Installed boiler capacity	Total cost
300kw	£45,000-70,000
1000kw	£65,000-85,000

Extra for pressurization equipment in lieu of feed and expansion tank cold feed and open vent.

300kw	£10,000
1000kw	£11,000

Packaged water boiler welded construction complete with boiler mountings and instruments, insulated casing, burner unit, delivery and commissioning.

Fuel	Rating	£
Gas	300kw	5,500
Gas	1000kw	13,000
Oil (35 sec)	300kw	4,500
Oil (35 sec)	1000kw	10,500

Chilled water plant

Chilled water plant comprising of:

2 nr packaged water cooled water chillers
2 nr pater cooling towers
2 nr end suction, direct driven condenser
water circulating pumps
2 nr end suction, direct driven, chilled
water circulating pumps
Interconnecting pipework, valves, fittings,
thermal insulation, automatic controls,
anti-vibration mountings, feed tank and
chemical water treatment, commissioning
and regulating valve sets

Cost per ton of cooling capacity   £1000-2000

Extra for use of dry coolers in
lieu of water cooling towers

Cost per ton of cooling capacity   £200

Ductwork

The rates given include for the sheet metal ductwork and associated fittings as listed. All labour and materials for the manufacture, delivery and erection for the fabrication of fittings and supports connections to either supplied or free issue equipment is included. Fittings and the like include, bends with turning vanes, tees equal and reducing, blank ends, transformations, flexible connections, diffuser and grille connections, stiffeners, branch spigots, volume control dampers, standard operated multi-leaf fire dampers, insulated access doors, flanges, tie rods, supports and brackets fixed to masonry construction. Also included is the pressure testing and cleaning of internal surface of ductwork, temporarily disconnection and reconnection of grilles and diffusers, setting to work and regulation of air system

Ductwork (cont'd)	Unit	£

Ductwork standard - HVCA DW 142

Circular low velocity galvanized mild steel ductwork (straight seams)	t	6,500
Circular high velocity galvanized mild steel ductwork (straight seams)	t	7,500
Rectangular low velocity galvanized mild steel ductwork	t	8,000
Rectangular high velocity galvanized mild steel ductwork	t	9,500

Air handling units

Packaged air handling unit comprising of:

Fresh/recirculated air mixing box
section fresh/exhaust/recirculated air
dampers
Bag filter assembly
Heating coil section
Centrifugal fan section
Installed in a double skin, modular framed
  enclosure and complete with access section,

  anti-vibration mountings and flexible
  connections. Unit suitable for external
  location

Air Volume vs External Resistance

2700 m3/hr vs 150 pa	nr	4,500
3600 m3/hr vs 250 pa	nr	5,000
7200 m3/hr vs 250 pa	nr	6,500
28800 m3/hr vs 500 pa	nr	17,500

Packaged air handling unit comprising of:

Fresh/recirculated air mixing box section
Fresh/exhaust/recirculated air dampers

Bag filter assembly
Main heating coil section
Cooling coil section
Re-heat section
Electric operation steam humidifier
Centrifugal fan section installed on a
    double skin, modular framed enclosure
    and complete with access sections, anti-
    vibration mountings, and flexible
    connections. Unit suitable for external location

Air Volume vs External Resistance		£
2700 m3/hr vs 150 pa	nr	9,500
3600 m3/hr vs 250 pa	nr	10,500
7200 m3/hr vs 250 pa	nr	13,500
28800 m3/hr vs 500 pa	nr	34,000

Axial fans

Aerofoil axial flow fan, long casing including supports, anti-vibration
mountings, standard flexible connections and matching flanges

Fan Diameter	Air Volume	External Resistance		£
300mm	1800 m3/hr	150 Pa	nr	400
300mm	1800 m3/hr	250 Pa	nr	450
475mm	3600 m3/hr	150 Pa	nr	500
475mm	3600 m3/hr	250 Pa	nr	550
610mm	5400 m3/hr	150 Pa	nr	625
610mm	5400 m3/hr	250 Pa	nr	675
760mm	7200 m3/hr	150 Pa	nr	750
760mm	7200 m3/hr	250 Pa	nr	825

Axial fans (cont'd)

Bi-furcated axial flow fan, for operating temperatures up to 200°C, including supports, anti-vibration mountings, high temperatures flexible connections and matching flanges

Fan Diameter	Air Volume	External Resistance		£
150 mm	1080 m3/hr	80 Pa	nr	400
200 mm	1440 m3/hr	100 Pa	nr	440
300 mm	2160 m3/hr	125 Pa	nr	500
375 mm	2880 m3/hr	150 Pa	nr	550

Air inlet and exhaust louvres   £

Anodized aluminium inlet and exhaust louvre complete with 100mm deep blades, flanged frame and bird proof mesh screen. Louvres fixed to timber frame provided by others.   m2   200

Extra for powder coating paint finish   m2   20

Fire fighting equipment

Wet and dry risers

100mm rising main including horizontal breeching inlet with 2 nr 64mm instantaneous couplings, inlet box, landing valves and boxes

Cost per landing   nr   900

Hose reels

Swing type automatic recessed hose reel complete with housing for building into masonary structure, 24 metres of hosing, isolation and drain valve   nr   650

Fire hydrants £

(Supply pipework measured elsewhere).

100mm pillar hydrant, cast iron sluice valve, flanged connections	nr	900
Underground hydrants to BS750 complete with sluice valve, flanged connections	nr	350

Sprinkler installation

The number of sprinkler heads required to provide the necessary degree of protection is determined by the hazard classification. The design of sprinkler installation should be carried out by registered companies who are on the Fire Office Committee (FOC) list.

As a guide either the cost per m2 of protected area or cost per head can be used. In both cases the rates cover for all associated pipework, valve sets, booster pumps and supports.

Cost for area protected	m2	£10.00-17.00
Cost per sprinkler head	nr	£150.00

(Storage and provision of standby power equipment is not included.)

Calorifiers

Copper storage calorifiers

Calorifiers to BS853 either horizontal or vertical pattern complete with cradle or legs, all pipe connections, mountings and instruments, thermostatic controls for primary side, temperature and pressure relief valves, mineral fibre thermal insulation and hammer clad aluminium finish. Heater battery fed with steam or LTHW as listed sized to raise stored water from $10^{\circ}C$ to $65^{\circ}C$ in one hour.

Copper storage calorifiers £

Heating Source - Steam (L.P.)

Capacity

500 litres	nr	1,400
1000 litres	nr	1.750
2000 litres	nr	2,450
3000 litres	nr	3,000

Heating Source - LTHW

Capacity

500 litres	nr	1,500
1000 litres	nr	2,000
2000 litres	nr	3,250
3000 litres	nr	4,000

Non-storage calorifiers

Steam fed non-storage calorifier providing LTHW service 82°C/71°C horizontal pattern ccomplete with supports, steam traps, sight glasses, valves, mineral fibre thermal insulation and hammer clad aluminium finish, temperature controls

Heating capacity £

100kw	nr	600
200kw	nr	750
300kw	nr	1,200
600kw	nr	2,000
1000kw	nr	3,300

ELECTRICAL WORK

Conduit systems

The following rates include for installing materials up to a maximum height of 4.5m, delivery, off loading storage, distribution up to room and wastage.

Galvanized heavy gauge steel conduit to BS4568 Class 4 inclusive of elbows, tees, circular steel boxes, intersections, saddles, clips and draw wires. Cable measured separately. Cable diameter

		Run on surface £	Run in chase £
16 mm	m	32.00	30.00
20 mm	m	34.00	32.00
25 mm	m	45.00	43.00
32 mm	m	54.00	52.00

Black enamel, heavy gauge, steel conduit to BS4568 class 2 inclusive of elbows, tees, circular steel boxes, intersections, saddles, clips and draw wires. Cable diameter

16 mm	m	26.00	24.00
20 mm	m	30.00	28.00
25 mm	m	36.00	34.00
32 mm	m	45.00	43.00

PVC conduit, super high impact, heavy gauge, inclusive of elbows, tees, circular steel boxes, intersections, saddles, clips and draw wires. Cable diameter

16 mm	m	22.00	20.00
20 mm	m	25.00	23.00
25 mm	m	33.00	30.00
32 mm	m	45.00	43.00

Trunking systems

Steel trunking single compartment,
heavy gauge galvanized to BS4678,
inclusive of full length lids, fillets,
gusset elbows, tees, fourway section,
blank ends, sleeve complings,
reducers, cable retainers, fire
barriers and supports

Trunking size		£
50 x 50mm	m	48.00
75 x 50mm	m	54.00
75 x 75mm	m	60.00
100 x 50mm	m	63.00
100 x 75mm	m	67.00
100 x 100mm	m	74.00
150 x 150mm	m	88.00
150 x 75mm	m	94.00
150 x 100mm	m	102.00
150 x 150mm	m	110.00
225 x 100mm	m	150.00

PVC trunking, single compartment
to BS4678 and 4607, inclusive of full
length lids, couplings, stop ends, flat
angles, internal/external angles, flat
tees, adaptors, side tees, intersections,
circular boxes and supports

mini-trunking

16 x 16mm	m	10.00
25 x 16mm	m	12.00

		£
32 x 12.5mm	m	12.00
40 x 16mm	m	14.00
40 x 25mm	m	16.00
40 x 40mm	m	22.00
50 x 25mm	m	20.00
50 x 32mm	m	22.00

standard trunking

50 x 50mm	m	54.00
75 x 50mm	m	58.00
75 x 75mm	m	72.00
100 x 50mm	m	80.00
100 x 75mm	m	90.00
100 x 100mm	m	102.00
150 x 75mm	m	170.00
150 x 100mm	m	210.00
150 x 150mm	m	220.00

Cables

Multicore armoured PVC insulated cables to BS6346 inclusive of all clips, fixings, cable terminations. Installed on surface, tray or trunking.

		2 core £	3 core £	4 core £
1.5mm2	m	4.00	4.00	5.00
2.5mm2	m	5.00	5.00	6.00
4mm2	m	7.00	8.00	12.00
6mm2	m	8.00	10.00	12.00

Cables (cont'd)

		2 core £	3 core £	4 core £
10mm2	m	12.00	15.00	16.00
16mm2	m	12.00	19.00	20.00

Single core PVC insulated cables,
non-armoured with sheath (twin and
earth) BS6004, inclusive of all clips,
fixings, installed on surface or in chases

		£
1.0mm2	m	2.00
1.5mm2	m	2.50
2.5mm2	m	3.00
4mm2	m	4.50
6mm2	m	6.50
10mm2	m	10.00
16mm2	m	15.00

Tray and ladder systems

Cable tray, standard pattern
heavy duty from perforated mild
steel to BS1449, hot dip galvanized,
inclusive of flat bends, outside/inside
risers, tees, 4-way cross pieces,
reducers, tray width

102mm, gauge 1.5mm	m	40.00
152mm, gauge 1.5mm	m	45.00
229mm, gauge 1.5mm	m	60.00
305mm, gauge 1.5mm	m	75.00
457mm, gauge 2.0mm	m	112.00
610mm, gauge 2.0mm	m	145.00

Cable tray, return flange, heavy
duty formed from perforated mild
steel to BS1449, hot dip galvanized,
inclusive of flat bends, outside/inside
risers, tees, 4-way cross pieces,
reducers, tray width

£

102mm, gauge 1.5mm	m	65.00
152mm, gauge 1.5mm	m	75.00
229mm, gauge 1.5mm	m	85.00
305mm, gauge 1.5mm	m	105.00
457mm, gauge 2.0mm	m	150.00
610mm, gauge 2.0mm	m	190.00

Cable ladders heavy duty, 130mm
deep, 2 mm gauge, formed from
mild steel to BS1449, galvanized to
BS729 inclusive of internal/external
riser, flat bends, equal tees, four way
cross pieces, reducers, couplers,
cantilever brackets, fixings and
supports, ladder width

152mm	m	120.00
302mm	m	135.00
452mm	m	150.00
602mm	m	165.00
752mm	m	185.00
902mm	m	195.00

Fire alarm systems

System and installation to BS5839 'Fire Detection and Alarm System in Buildings', Local Fire Officer but excluding the requirements of the Employers' Insurers. Each zone and sounder circuit is monitored. Battery back up for 72 hours provided. Fire alarm panel to BS3116 part 4. Wiring in red over sheath MICV cable inclusive of all clips, fastenings and terminations.

Rates inclusive of system commissioning by the fire alarm equipment manufacturer

		£
break glass	nr	105.00
bell	nr	120.00
heat detector	nr	130.00
smoke detector	nr	130.00

Extra for zone panel, battery charger

4 zone	nr	775.00
8 zone	nr	1,300.00
16 zone	nr	1,750.00
Extra for repeater panel	nr	400.00

Lightning protection

Lightning protection system and installation to BS6651 "Protection of Structures against Lightning". System comprises of air termination, down conductors, earth rods, clips and fastenings, junction clamps, disconnection links, rod to cable lugs and sockets, total area of building protected

750m2	nr	5,000.00
1600m2	nr	7,000.00
3600m2	nr	9,000.00

Power and lighting installations   £

Power

Rates for the wiring of power points
including switched socket outlets,
fused spurs, consumer unit, fixings,
conduit system and associated components
as applicable. Accessories used are of
high impact plastic manufacture.

Power point PVC twin and earth cable in residential property on ring main with MCB circuit protection	nr	45.00
PVC insulated cables on galvanized conduit system in commercial property	nr	80.00
PVC insulated cables in galvanized conduit system in industrial property	nr	90.00

Extra for

110v industrial circuit transformer (30VA)	nr	28.00
110v socket complete with isolator	nr	65.00
415v 16 amp socket complete with RCD protection (30mA)	nr	145.00
45 amp cooker control unit	nr	14.00
shaver socket	nr	30.00
1.7kw storage heater	nr	165.00
2.5kw storage heater	nr	215.00
3.4kw storage heater	nr	250.00

Power installations (cont'd)   £

Busbar installation, maximum
rating 200 amp, inclusive of
end connection isolator units,
supports and fixings to
masonry construction

length 15m	m	30.00
length 30m	m	50.00
length 60m	m	85.00
Extra over for fused tap-in box	nr	55.00
Extra over for isolator fused tap-in box	nr	100.00

Lighting

Rates for the wiring of lighting points including light switch,
connection unit and accessories but excluding lighting fittings,
wiring from consumer unit or distribution board.

Lighting points

PVC twin and earth cable in residential property, chased into plaster, covered in PVC sheath	nr	45.00
PVC insulated cables in galvanized conduit system in commercial property	nr	95.00
PVC insulated cables in galvanized conduit system in industrial property	nr	110.00

Extra for luminaires as listed inclusive of supports, flexible cable,
connector blocks, control gear, conduit boxes, fixed to a masonry
construction. Lamp and opal diffuser included in price where applicab

Fluorescent tubes (standard)		£
1 x 18W, length 600mm	nr	22.00
2 x 18W, length 600mm	nr	35.00
1 x 36W, length 1200mm	nr	30.00
2 x 36W, length 1200mm	nr	50.00
1 x 58W, length 1500mm	nr	35.00
2 x 58W, length 1500mm	nr	60.00
1 x 70W, length 1800mm	nr	40.00
2 x 70W, length 1800mm	nr	65.00
1 x 100W, length 2400mm	nr	55.00
2 x 100W, length 2400mm	nr	85.00
Fluorescent tubes (emergency)		
1 x 36W, length 1200mm	nr	175.00
2 x 36W, length 1200mm	nr	220.00
1 x 58W, length 1500mm	nr	140.00
2 x 58W, length 1500mm	nr	165.00
1 x 70W, length 1800mm	nr	180.00
2 x 70W, length 1800mm	nr	200.00
1 x 100W, length 2400mm	nr	210.00
2 x 100W, length 2400mm	nr	235.00

Range of prices cover for lamp type, luminaire type, finish, fixings, adjustable, recessed, wall or ceiling mountings.

Luminaire	nr	20.00

Industrial lighting	Unit	£
high bay luminaires		
150W SON lamp	nr	215.00
250W SON lamp	nr	235.00
400W SON lamp	nr	260.00
low bay luminaires		
150W SON/T lamp	nr	175.00
250W SON/T lamp	nr	190.00
400W SON/T lamp	nr	210.00
heavy duty bulkhead luminaires		
80w HPL-N lamps	nr	145.00
80w HPL-N lamp (Zone 2)	nr	155.00
Floodlights		
SOX - E66 lamp	nr	244.00
400w SON/T lamp	nr	284.00
400w HPI/T lamp	nr	329.00

Incoming mains and switch gear installation

Internally located substation equipment, comprising of HV switchgear, 1 nr 1000 DVA transformer complete with Bukholtz relay, link disconnection unit, LV switch board, interconnecting cabling, electronic fault detection relays, inter-trip relays, cabling, break glasses, 30v dc supply, delivery, installation, works and site testing and commissioning.

Approximate cost   £70,000

Incoming mains and switch
gear installation (cont'd)

Main building, switch board panel, of modular construction.
Maximum rating 800 amps, inclusive of delivery, off loading,
site assembly, making all final cable connections,
instrumentation and testing.

   Approximate cost   £10,000

The above figures can vary substantially depending on the complexity
and requirements of the installation, location of site and local
electricity authority requirements and the necessary adjustments must
be made.

Lift and escalator installation	Unit	£
Lifts		

The following rates assume a
floor to floor height of 3 metres
with standard finish to cars and
doors.

Passenger lifts

	Unit	£
Electrically operated, 8/10 person lift serving 6 levels and travel speed of 1 metre/second.	nr	50,000
Extra for bottom motor room	nr	3,000
Extra levels served	nr	2,500
Increased speed of travel		
1 to 1.6 metre/second	nr	2,500
1 to 2.5 metre/second	nr	30,000
Enhanced finish to car	nr	6,500
Electrically operated 21 person lift serving 6 levels and travel speed of 1 metre/second.	nr	62,000

Passenger lifts (cont'd)	Unit	£
Extra for bottom motor room	nr	3,500
Extra levels served	nr	2,750
Increased speed of travel		
1.6 to 2.5 metre/second	nr	30,000
Enhanced finish to car	nr	7,000

Goods lifts

	Unit	£
Electrically operated, two speed, general purpose lift serving 5 levels, maximum load 500 kg, manually operated shutters and automatic push button control, with a travel speed of 0.25m/s	nr	32,000
Extra levels served	nr	2,500
Increased capacity to 2000kg	nr	12,000
Increased travel speed 0.25 to 0.5 metre/second	nr	2,000
Electrically operated heavy duty goods lift serving 5 levels, maximum load 1500 kg, with manually operated doors and automatic push button control and speed of 0.25 metre/second.	nr	38,000
Increased capacity to 3000kg	nr	18,000
Extra levels served	nr	2,500
Through car	nr	3,000

	Unit	£
Oil hydraulic operated, heavy duty goods lift serving 4 levels, to take 500 kg load with manually operated shutters and automatic push button control and speed of 0.25 metre/second.	nr	42,000
Increased capacity to 1000kg	nr	2,500
Increased capacity to 1500kg	nr	4,250
Increased capacity to 2000kg	nr	8,500

Escalator installation

30° pitch escalator with a rise of 3.5 metres and enamelled sheet steel or glass balustrades.

	Unit	£
600mm tread	nr	35,000
800mm tread	nr	38,000
1000mm tread	nr	40,000

Extra for

	Unit	£
stainless steel balustrades	nr	1,500
glass balustrades with lighting	nr	1,500

Part Four

Reclamation and Landscaping

Site clearance	Unit	£
Cut down trees, grub up roots		
600mm to 1.5m girth	nr	80.00
1.5 to 3.0m girth	nr	100.00
Cut down hawthorn hedge, grub up roots		
1500mm high	m	5.00
3000mm high	m	6.00
Clear site of undergrowth and vegetation	m2	0.10
Excavate topsoil, lay aside for reuse, average depth		
150mm	m2	0.20
200mm	m2	0.40
Excavate from ground level to reduce levels, maximum depth not exceeding		
0.25m	m3	3.00
1.00m	m3	2.50
2.00m	m3	3.00
Extra for breaking up by compressor and tools		
concrete 100mm thick	m2	4.00
tarmacadam 75mm thick	m2	3.00
hardcore 100mm thick	m2	3.00
plain concrete	m3	3.00
reinforced concrete	m3	40.00
soft rock	m3	41.00
hard rock	m3	43.00

Site clearance (cont'd)	Unit	£
Load surplus excavated material into barrows, wheel and deposit in temporary spoil heaps, average distance		
25m	m3	10.00
50m	m3	17.00
Load surplus excavated material by machine direct from excavation and remove to 19Km distance	m3	8.00
Load surplus excavated material by machine from spoil heaps and remove to tip 10Km distance	m3	11.00

FILLING

Imported filling material deposited on site in layers not exceeding 250mm thick, average distance 25m, compacting with vibrating roller

surplus exavated material	m3	8.00
sand	m3	23.00
topsoil	m3	18.00
subsoil	m3	13.00
granular material DTp type 1	m3	17.00
granular material DTp type 2	m3	17.00
rock	m3	16.00

SURFACE TREATMENTS

Break up existing ground with plough or rotovator, depth

100mm	100m2	10.00
200mm	100m2	13.00
300mm	100m2	14.00
400mm	100m2	16.00

	Unit	£
Cultivate ploughed ground with disc, drag or chain harrow, 4 passes	100m2	10.00
Roll cultivated ground self-propelled roller	100m2	5.00

SOIL STABILIZATION

Crib retaining walling consisting of impregnated timber constructed in accordance with the manufacturer's instructions, model

440 (retaining up to 1m)	m2	50.00
550 Key block (retaining up to 1.5m)	m2	70.00
1100 (retaining up to 5.9m)	m2	230.00
1375 (retaining up to 7.4m)	m2	300.00

Gabions

Maccferri box gabions placed n position filled with stone

zinc coated	m3	35.00
PVC coated	m3	50.00

Flexible sheeting

Paraweb' flexible sheeting Type 1005 laid on prepared ground

Mono	m2	9.00
Duplex	m2	10.00
Triplex	m2	12.00

Polypropylene sheeting laid on prepared ground

G-100 0.6mm thick	m2	1.10
F-2B 0.95mm thick	m2	1.30
F-32M 2.5mm thick	m2	1.70

Flexible sheeting (cont'd)	Unit	£
'Tensar' polypropylene ground stabilising mat fixed to ground with steel pegs	m2	3.20
'Tensar' polyethylene ground stabilising mat fixed to ground with steel pegs	m2	6.00

'Greenfix' biodegradable erosion control mats fixed with pins to prepared ground

Seeded

type 1 Cavamat Standard	m2	3.30
type 2 Cavamat Special	m2	4.00
type 3 Cavamat Coco	m2	5.00
type 14 Fibremat	m2	6.00

Unseeded

type 4 Eromat Light	m2	2.50
type 5 Eromat Special	m2	3.00
type 6 Cocomat Special	m2	4.00
type 7 Cocomat heavy	m2	5.00
type 13 Fibremat	m2	6.00

Mulchmat

type 9 Standard	m2	3.00
type 10 Special	m2	4.00

Terram

Polypropylene sheeting laid on prepared ground, type

500	m2	0.70
700	m2	0.90
1000	m2	1.00
2000	m2	2.00

	Unit	£

INTERLOCKING BRICK/BLOCK PAVINGS

Charcon Europa block paving, size

200 x 100 x 65mm, natural	m2	20.00
200 x 100 x 80mm, natural	m2	23.00
200 x 100 x 65mm, coloured	m2	22.00
200 x 100 x 80mm, coloured	m2	25.00

Marshalls Keyblock concrete paving natural colour, size

200 x 100 x 65mm	m2	15.00
200 x 100 x 80mm	m2	16.00

Marshalls Keyblock concrete paving coloured, size

200 x 100 x 65mm	m2	16.00
200 x 100 x 80mm	m2	18.00

Charcon Europa grassgrid, size

366 x 274 x 100mm	m2	17.00

Ibstock brick pavings size 200 x 100 x 65mm, laid to falls on prepared surfaces

Red chamfered

straight joints both ways		
bricks laid flat	m2	28.00
bricks laid on edge	m2	40.00

herringbone pattern

bricks laid flat	m2	30.00
bricks laid on edge	m2	42.00

	Unit	£

Paving slabs

Precast concrete paving flags,
spot bedded in cement lime
mortar (1:1:6), size

plain colour

	Unit	£
900 x 600 x 50mm	m2	11.50
750 x 600 x 50mm	m2	12.00
600 x 600 x 50mm	m2	13.00
450 x 600 x 50mm	m2	15.00

coloured

	Unit	£
900 x 600 x 50mm	m2	11.50
750 x 600 x 50mm	m2	12.00
600 x 600 x 50mm	m2	13.00
450 x 600 x 50mm	m2	15.00

Marshalls pressed paving
flags, hexagonal, 400mm
across flats, natural colour

full flag

	Unit	£
Saxon	m2	19.00
Perfecta	m2	24.00

half flag

	Unit	£
Saxon	m2	15.00
Perfecta	m2	17.00

Marshalls pressed paving
flags, horizontal, 400mm
across flats, red or buff

full flag

	Unit	£
Saxon	m2	21.00
Perfecta	m2	26.00

half flag

	Unit	£
Saxon	m2	16.00
Perfecta	m2	18.00

	Unit	£

SEEDING/TURFING

Pre-seeding work (by machine)

Lift topsoil from spoil
heap and spread in layers,
thickness

	Unit	£
50mm	100m2	27.00
75mm	100m2	35.00
100m	100m2	45.00

Harrow topsoil to fine tilth, depth

	Unit	£
50mm	100m2	5.50
75mm	100m2	6.00
100m	100m2	6.50

Grass seeding (by machine)

**Supply and sow grass seed in
two operations**

Booker grass seeds

	Unit	£
parks	100m2	5.00
suburban	100m2	5.00
estate	100m2	6.00
MOT mix	100m2	5.00
formal	100m2	13.00
elite	100m2	23.00
outfield	100m2	11.00
greensward	100m2	10.00
low maintenance	100m2	9.00
low fertility landscapes	100m2	9.00
Cumberland	100m2	16.00
green	100m2	13.00
undertrees	100m2	14.00
prizelawn	100m2	18.00
tufflawn	100m2	10.00
quicksport	100m2	15.00
fineturf	100m2	18.00
cricket square	100m2	18.00
Wembley football	100m2	8.00
action replay	100m2	7.00
classic mixture	100m2	7.00

	Unit	£
Supply and spread fertiliser to prepared ground (35g/m2)		
ammonium sulphate	100m2	2.00
nitrochalk	100m2	3.00
potassium nitrate	100m2	3.50
sodium nitrate	100m2	3.00
urea	100m2	3.00
super phosphate	100m2	2.50
triple superphosphate	100m2	3.00
potassium sulphate	100m2	3.00
magnesium sulphate	100m2	2.50
bonemeal	100m2	3.00
dried blood	100m2	4.50
hoof and horn	100m2	4.00
fish, blood and stone	100m2	2.50

**Post seeding treatment
(by machine)**

	Unit	£
Treat seeded area with light chain harrow	100m2	3.00

Turfing

Lay imported turves size 4000 x
2000 x 19mm on prepared bed

	Unit	£
untreated meadow turf	m2	2.00

Rolawn

	Unit	£
Advantage	m2	4.00
Select	m2	4.00
Olympic	m2	4.00
Medallion	m2	3.00
Sports	m2	3.00
Luxury	m2	5.00
Treat turves with wooden paddle beater	m2	0.25
Treat turves with light roller	m2	0.20

	Unit	£
First cut to turves 20mm high with man-operated power driven cylinder mower including boxing cuttings	m2	0.20

Trees

Excavate for and plant
transplants or seedling,
backfill and water, plant cost

£0.50	nr	1.00
£1.00	nr	1.60
£2.50	nr	3.50

Excavate tree pit, fork bottom,
plant containerized tree,
backfill, water, surround with
peat (1 stake and 2 ties per
tree), tree cost

£5.00 (180cm high)	nr	7.50
£15.00 (210cm high)	nr	20.00
£30.00 (10cm girth)	nr	50.00
£50.00 (14cm girth)	nr	75.00
£100.00 (22cm girth)	nr	190.00

Excavate tree pit, fork bottom,
plant bare root tree, backfill,
water surround with peat (1
stake and 2 ties per tree),
tree cost

£10.00 (8cm girth)	nr	20.00
£40.00 (14cm girth)	nr	80.00
£75.00 (16cm girth)	nr	130.00

Excavate tree pit, fork bottom,
plant conifer, backfill, water
surround with peat (1 stake and
2 ties per tree), tree cost

£3.00 (40cm high)	nr	5.00
£20.00 (180cm high)	nr	27.00

Trees (cont'd)	Unit	£
Form planting hole in cultivated area, plant shrub, backfill, water, surround with peat, shrub cost		
£5.00 (90cm high)	nr	7.00
£10.00 (120cm high)	nr	14.00

Seating

The following seating is assumed to be bolted to existing concrete surfaces

Teak seating (Barlow Tyrie Ltd)

Braintree IBR15 length 1500mm	nr	170.00
Glenham IGL15	nr	240.00
Glenham IGL18 length 1800mm	nr	310.00

Cast iron seating (Townscape Products Ltd)

Baltimore bench	nr	350.00
Standard Baltimore seat	nr	510.00

Planters

Steel and hardwood planters (Townscape Products Ltd)

Sovereign square

500 x 500 x 470mm high	nr	430.00
500 x 500 x 670mm high	nr	480.00
750 x 750 x 870mm high	nr	610.00
1000 x 1000 x 470mm high	nr	560.00
1500 x 1000 x 670mm high	nr	740.00
1500 x 1000 x 870mm high	nr	810.00

Sovereign rectangular

750 x 500 x 470mm high	nr	450.00
750 x 500 x 670mm high	nr	510.00
1000 x 750 x 670mm high	nr	580.00

	Unit	£
1000 x 750 x 870mm high	nr	630.00
1500 x 1000 x 670mm high	nr	740.00
1500 x 1000 x 870mm high	nr	810.00

Litter bins

Steel and cast iron litter bins
(Townscape Products Ltd)

Baltimore Major	nr	390.00
Baltimore Minor	nr	360.00
Baltimore Half	nr	270.00

Cycle holders

| Penny cycle stand bollard with 8 holders | nr | 360.00 |
| Concrete cycle block, exposed aggregate | nr | 24.00 |

Bollards

Galvanised steel bollards
(Townscape Products Ltd)

Grenadier	nr	140.00
Grenadier Major	nr	170.00
Coldstream	nr	113.00

Cast iron bollards
(Townscape Products Ltd)

Tudor	nr	260.00
Elizabethan	nr	310.00
Capstan	nr	320.00

Exposed aggregate concrete
bollards (Townscape Products
Ltd)

| Quartet | nr | 100.00 |
| Penny | nr | 130.00 |

Special surfacing

Playtop '85' impact absorbing safety surfacing laid on existing surfaces from Charles Lawrence UK Ltd	Unit	Black	Coloured
		£	£
25mm to falls, cross falls	m2	28	50
60mm to falls, cross falls	m2	50	70
80mm to falls, cross falls	m2	55	80
100mm to falls, cross falls	m2	60	85

Fire paths

Grass concrete paving using polystyrene formers and grass seed

100mm thick	m2	16
150mm thick	m2	20

Fencing

Chainlink fencing fixed to concrete posts with galvanised wire, height

900mm	m	12
1400mm	m	15
1800mm	m	18

Timber post and rail fence with three rails fixed to posts at 2m centres, height 1200mm   m   8

Post and wire fencing consisting of round wire stapled to timber posts

3 strand	m	7
4 strand	m	8
5 strand	m	9

MAINTENANCE OF SEEDED AND TURFED AREAS

	Unit	£
Pick up litter by hand and remove	100m2	1.00
Sweep up leaves with motorised vacuum cleaner and remove	100m2	4.00
Cut grass to specified height using		
multi-unit mower	100m2	0.30
3 gang mower	100m2	0.40
ride-on triple cylinder mower	100m2	0.40
ride-on triple rotary mower	100m2	1.40
man-operated power driven cylinder mower	100m2	2.20
man-operated power driven rotary mower	100m2	2.00
power flail cutter	100m2	2.40
fine cut with hand operated cylinder mower	100m2	3.30
scythe	100m2	8.90
Extra for boxing cuttings	100m2	0.70
Extra for raking up loose grass and placing in heaps for disposal	100m2	2.00
Trim edges of grassed areas using		
non-mechanical edging tool	100m	12.50
strimmer	100m	7.30

Maintenance of seeded and turfed areas (cont'd)	Unit	£
Aerate grass areas, 100mm depth, using		
man operated power driven slitter aerator	100m2	3.00
fork	100m2	15.00
tractor drawn aerator	100m2	1.00
Extra for sweeping up corings and placing in heap for disposal	100m2	8.10
Scarify grass areas to break up thatch and remove dead growth		
man -operated scarifer and placing in heaps for disposal	100m2	4.00
tractor drawn scarifer	100m2	1.00
Harrow grass areas using		
chain harrow	100m2	3.50
drag mat (by hand)	100m2	4.10
Remove stones and debris from grassed areas and placing in spoil heaps for disposal, size exceeding		
15mm	100m2	40.50
25mm	100m2	32.50
50mm	100m2	10.00
Apply selective weedkiller in accordance with manufacturer's instructions	100m2	53.00
Supply and spread fertiliser to prepared ground (35g/m2)		
ammonium sulphate	100m2	2.20
nitrochalk	100m2	2.90
potassium nitrate	100m2	3.20
sodium nitrate	100m2	2.40

	Unit	£
urea	100m2	2.60
super phosphate	100m2	2.30
triple superphosphate	100m2	2.70
potassium sulphate	100m2	2.80
magnesium sulphate	100m2	2.50
bonemeal	100m2	3.10
dried blood	100m2	4.30
hoof and horn	100m2	4.00
fish, blood and stone	100m2	2.20

MAINTENANCE OF PLANTED AREAS

Spread fine grade bark mulch,
thickness

	Unit	£
25mm	100m2	160.00
50mm	100m2	220.00
75mm	100m2	320.00

Spread medium grade bark
mulch, thickness

	Unit	£
75mm	100m2	120.00
100mm	100m2	164.00
150mm	100m2	242.00

Spread coarse grade bark
mulch, thickness

	Unit	£
75mm	100m2	145.00
100mm	100m2	197.00
150mm	100m2	290.00

Weed and hoe planted areas,
place weeds in spoil heaps
for disposal — 100m2 — 25.00

Remove stones and debris
from grassed areas and place
in spoil heaps for disposal,
size exceeding

	Unit	£
15mm	100m2	41.00
25mm	100m2	33.00
50mm	100m2	10.00

Maintenance of planted areas (cont'd)	Unit	£
Apply selective weedkiller in accordance with manufacturer's instructions	100m2	29.00
Supply and spread herbicide (£3 per kg) to prepared ground		
35g/m2	100m2	14.00
70g/m2	100m2	27.00
100g/m2	100m2	37.00
150g/m2	100m2	56.00

Part Five

Alterations and Repairs

11 Principal rates

BUILDING WORK

Demolition

Demolition of entire structures are costed by the volume of the building and the following are a guide for small buildings. For large buildings competitive quotations should be obtained because the value of the salvaged material can have a considerable effect on the price charged.

	Unit	£
Single storey brick buildings (50-100m3)	m3	7
Single storey brick buildings (100-200m3)	m3	6
Two storey brick buildings (200-400m3)	m3	4

Alterations internally

Cutting openings size 1.5-2.0m2 through walls

150mm blockwork	nr	250-350
225mm brickwork	nr	375-500

Taking down walls

partition, 100-150mm blockwork	m2	7-10
brickwork		
half brick thick	m2	10-15
one brick thick	m2	15-20

Alterations internally (cont'd)	Unit	£
Fill openings in walls		
partition, 100-150mm blockwork	m2	20-25
brickwork		
half brick thick	m2	35-40
one brick thick	m2	60-70
Taking out fireplaces and fill openings only	nr	50-100
Cutting holes through floors for stair 2-3m2 in reinforced concrete, thickness		
150mm	nr	450-500
225mm	nr	650-1000
Take out timber stair and fill in timber floor opening	nr	150-250
Taking out bathroom fittings per bathroom	nr	150-200
Taking out kitchen fittings per kitchen	nr	100-150
Taking up floor coverings and making good surface to receive new covering		
timber including removing nails	m2	3-5
screed including making good	m2	5-7
Taking up skirtings, dado rails	m	1-2
Pull down ceilings prepare to receive new ceiling finishes	m2	2-5
Hack off wall finishings	m2	2-5

	Unit	£
Alterations externally		
Take off roof coverings		
tile and dispose	m2	3-4
slates and set aside for reuse	m2	4-6
asphalt roofing and skirtings	m2	7-9
Extra for asbestos or other toxic waste products	m2	25-30
Take down gutters and fascia boards	m	2-5
Take down chimney stack to below roof slope	nr	300-350
Take down chimney breast from roof to ground floor	nr	1000-1250
Forming large opening in walls (up to 5m2)	nr	250-350
Allowance for erecting screens	m2	10-20
Provision of raking shores to two storey building	nr	300-400
Provision of dead shores to first floor level	nr	200-300
Defective concrete repairs		
Cutting out cracks in concrete and renovating	m	5-10
Filling openings in floors with new reinforced concrete bonded to existing		
150mm thick	m2	35-40
250mm thick	m2	45-50

CIVIL ENGINEERING WORK	Unit	£
Inserting additional beams under existing concrete floors (0.25-0.50 m2)	m	250-300
Inserting additional columns	m	500-750
Forming new bases in existing basement	nr	1500-3000
Cutting through reinforced concrete		
floors 250mm thick	m2	65-75
walls 150mm thick	m2	50-60

Structural steelwork

Taking down existing steel beam encased in concrete, renewing with larger and casing in concrete	m	200-250
Erecting new column 3m high including providing new base in existing floor making good, casing in concrete and making connections	nr	3000-4000

Part Six

General Cost Data

12

Life cycle costing

Introduction

Life cycle costing is a system for budgeting and controlling the costs of the design, development and property management of a building. It should focus on the building owner's policy requirement for the building.

The life cycle cost of a building is the total cost commitment to that building. It is the sum of the initial capital costs and the future running costs. These costs are incurred at different times and so they need to be discounted back to the present to allow them to be compared to the initial capital costs. There are standard techniques and published tables for discounting future costs and expressing them as a single sum of money (Net Present Value or NPV) or as an annual flow of money (Annual Equivalent).

Definitions

A range of terms are used in life cycle costing and the meanings of the most common terms are defined below.

Life cycle cost planning

The systematic and objective quantification of the initial and life time costs of a building or a building element at the design stage to produce a scheme which satisfies the client's objectives.

Costs in use

The technique of converting the life time cost consequences of a particular design decision into a single consistent measure of cost which can be used for comparison purposes. The 'measure' may be a single sum of money (NPV), a flow of money per time period (Annual Equivalent) or it may be expressed in terms of scarce resources whose use is to be minimised such as energy or manpower.

Life cycle cost analysis

The systematic collection and analysis of the running costs and performance characteristics of a building in use. The analysis should reflect the degree to which the costs incurred are justifiable in terms of the performance delivered.

The purpose of the analysis is to provide appropriately structured and processed data which can be used to prepare life cycle cost plans for new buildings or the life cycle cost management of an existing building.

Life cycle cost management

The process for developing and implementing a maintenance policy which recognizes that the building owner's or occupier's interest may be served best by setting maintenance decisions into his broader financial context and in a time frame which goes beyond the immediate maintenance horizon. The purpose of life cycle cost management is to establish maintenance management as a creative activity rather than one which is routine or reactive.

Approach

The inherent weakness of life cycle cost studies is that the formative influences on a building's life cycle characteristics are the decisions taken at the early design stages when there is little or no project specific information available which can be used to test the validity of those early decisions. Furthermore, the appraisal of design options for life cycle costing purposes must assume that cost implications can be reliably predicted for many years into the future. This is a somewhat fragile assumption given the long life of buildings and that the costs themselves are the result of a complex interplay between performance, use behaviour and changes in the economic environment.

The main emphasis for the developer or owner of the building should be to concentrate on generating an outline brief and management policy in life cycle terms. Concentrating on the outline brief has the significant benefit of defining the objectives for the completed development at a stage when they are still capable of affecting design decisions. The attention paid to formulating a management policy recognizes the fact that costs over the life of a building become less and less predictable the further they are removed from the present. The owner's interests may be served also, therefore, by adopting a system which can deal with these future costs as and when they arise in a manner which is consistent with the project's objectives, which themselves will have developed from the initial definition.

The intermediate stages between the outline brief at the commencement of design and the management policy for the building in use, should be used to translate the original requirements into a physical structure which is sufficiently robust to allow subsequent management decisions to moderate its performance in response to evolving objectives and environment conditions.

Benefits

The benefit of adopting a life cycle approach comes from the recognition that buildings are a long term investment. Assessing buildings' value from the initial capital costs is inconsistent with their long term nature and so attention should also be given to the future costs of buildings. Their design should result from decisions which recognize the objectives for the building over its whole life cycle.

Checklist for life cycle costing at outline brief stage (used to prepare life cycle cost plan)

Define objectives

Establish client's interest e.g. owner occupation - develop and lease - develop and sell.

Establish client's time horizon e.g. short term (develop) - medium term (develop and own for a limited period) - long term (develop and own long term).

Establish time horizon over which client's objectives will remain stable.

Establish client's specific space requirements, if for owner occupation.

Establish nature of tenants, if for leasing e.g. known tenants with known preferences - speculated tenant groups with open requirements.

Establish nature of lease and service charges, if tenanted e.g. - type and duration of lease - rent and service charge mix - division of responsibility between owner and tenants - basis of apportionment between tenants.

Establish importance of the project realizing a capital asset, and over what time scale this realization should take place.

Establish if there is a proposed purchaser and, if so, what his preferred requirements are.

Fit the project into the client's financial strategy

Establish the proposed method of finance e.g. development finance - finance during holding period - long term finance.

Establish impact of project on client's cash flow e.g. during development - during ownership - during redevelopment, refurbishment and disposal.

Establish effects on client's capital structure e.g. gearing and other ratios - effects on future financing options - effects on market capitalization both current and future.

Fit the project into the Client's main business strategy

Establish what resources the Client can apply to the project to - develop the project - actively manage the project (who and how) - manage the completed development.

Consider the time related variables

Establish the life cycles e.g. physical life of structure and key elements - economic life related to underlying land values - functional life - social life - leasehold cycles.

Establish the coincidence of the Client's requirements with the above life cycles.

Establish time related operational constraints e.g. the criticality of the completion date.

Establish the time related marketing constraints.

Establish the time related financial constraints e.g. the running out of a line of credit.

Establish the time related contractual constraints.

Establish the time related statutory constraints e.g. changes in taxation or building regulations.

Establish time related political constraints.

Consider the finance related variables

Establish the Client's investment criteria e.g. payback - DCF - ROCE.

Establish whether the criteria measure what it is that the Client is trying to achieve.

Establish the financial objectives e.g. maximize potential for rental income - maximize potential for cash generation - minimize running cost for owner occupier - secure long term capital growth.

Establish whether the funding arrangements mean that the project must achieve a particular asset value within a specific period of time.

Establish the Client's capital and revenue constraints and how they impact on the viability of the project e.g. cost yardsticks - financial or operational criteria - allowances for enhancement or avoidance.

Establish whether the residual value of the project has a significant impact on its viability. If so, is this at the termination of the project's life - at significant intervals - annually for valuation purposes.

Establish the relationship between the value of the project and the underlying land value.

Establish whether the ownership strategy envisages funds becoming available during the life of the project to counteract the effects of value depreciation relative to newer buildings coming on to the market.

Establish to what extent there is a trade off between capital and revenue.

Establish the client's attitude to risk both during development and ownership.

Establish the importance of the client's tax position regarding - the timing of cash flows - the capital cost/running cost relationship - capital gains tax, or relief therefrom.

Establish whether the tax status of the prospective tenant or purchaser impacts significantly on the client's objectives.

Establish what the tax implications surrounding the project are e.g. capital allowances - rates.

Establish whether the location of the project has fiscal implications e.g. grants - tax allowances - rates relief.

Consider the design-related variables

Establish the extent of finish for the completed development e.g. shell and core - ready to decorate - ready to occupy.

Establish the quality of finish for the completed development e.g. external envelope - internal furnishings and fixtures - public and common areas - general accommodation.

Establish the degree of structural flexibility required to cater for probable or possible future developments.

Establish the degree of superficial flexibility required to cater for e.g. changes in the image of the building - changes in the function of the building.

Establish the importance of cost and time trade-offs to the maintenance and refurbishment of the building in use e.g. will disruption costs be high - will rental losses be high.

Establish whether the local economy can provide for - the type of construction envisaged - the quality of fixtures and fittings envisaged - the level of maintenance envisaged.

Compile the external variables

Establish a weighted discount rate e.g. short term - long term - relative to the source of finance - relative to opportunity costs.

Establish inflation rates for e.g. project costs - operating costs - project revenues - tax position of client or occupier.

Establish commercial risk and relate to - choice of contract - maintenance contract - best and worst scenarios of key cost elements.

Establish political risk e.g. potential changes in direct taxation and tax allowances - potential changes in indirect taxation - potential changes in local taxation - susceptibility of financial arrangements to political change.

Development of a management policy

Once the building has been occupied information should be generated defining its true performance in use. At this stage it should be possible to establish a programme of maintenance, repair and refurbishment which accurately reflects the interplay between the client's objectives and the performance of the building i.e. life cycle management.

A worked example of a life cycle cost plan

Background information

Job title	:	New warehouse
Location	:	North West England
Client	:	Private development
Date	:	January 1990
Discount rate	:	8% (cost of capital = 17%; inflation @ 8%; discount rate = 1.17/1.08 = 8%)
Life cycle	:	20 years
Job details	:	Steel portal framed single storey building, including external works and drainage
Area	:	60,000 sq. ft.

LIFE CYCLE COST PLAN   £

1. Capital cost

Building; 60,000 sq ft @ £30	=	1,800,000
External works (approx. quants)	=	300,000
Contingencies @ 25% (client; design; contract)		525,000
Design fee @ 12.5%		325,000
		£ 2,950,000

2. Operating costs (annual)

2.1	General and water rates	= £	75,000 p.a.
	present value (20 years)	=	735,000
2.2	Heating and lighting	=	125,000 p.a.
	present value		1,225,000
2.3	General maintenance and insurance	= £	25,000 p.a.
	present value	=	245,000
		£	2,205,000

3. Repair and replacement costs (intermittent)

3.1 Redecorate every 3 years @ £2,000, present value	=		5,000
3.2 Re-carpet every 5 years @ £10,000, present value	=		15,000
3.3 Lighting and power refurbishment every 10 years @ £10,000, present value	=		5,000
		£	25,000

LIFE CYCLE COST PLAN SUMMARY

Summary of costs	Present Value
	£
1. Capital cost	2,950,000
2. Running cost - operating	2,205,000
- repair and replacement	25,000
TOTAL PRESENT VALUE £	5,180,000

13

The development process

Attempting to explain 'the development process' in one chapter is like being asked to write a do-it-yourself guide to open heart surgery! There are excellent books covering the whole subject which are available to readers who wish to become totally involved in the subjectbut the following should provide an overview and an awareness to those professionals not directly involved in the development scheme. Those parties on the fringe of a project should realize the importance of their part in the success of any one development, whether it is a new-build, a refurbishment or a break-up of an existing building complex.

The model chosen is a 3 acre industrial site in the North West of England for the design and build of new industrial/warehouse units. The model could just as easily have been an existing food store for break up into smaller units or a listed office building to be refurbished the principles are the same. It may help at this stage to clarify the main players involved in any development, i.e. The Professional Team, their role and where they appear in the scheme.

The agent

Very often the agent/development surveyor will find a site and introduce it to the developer who in his opinion is the most suitable to carry out the scheme. The agent will consider the developer's own expertise in property, his track record in development, his financial status and his capability to handle the overall project by bringing together the various members of the team. The agent may be a member of the RICS/ISVA although this is certainly not essential. Individually the agent may have the necessary skills to value the site, let the completed buildings, and provide the necessary advice to secure funding for the development. Alternatively, he may bring in assistance either from within his own firm or from outside depending upon the size of the scheme and the size of the agent's firm, and also whether he is a sole practitioner or is one of the larger firms of international property consultants.

The agent therefore advises in the acquisition, the letting, the sale of the investment and will most probably provide expert input throughout the scheme. He will probably advise on the specification of the buildings and the construction of the leases to make them acceptable to the tenant and to the institutional funding market.

The solicitor

A solicitor will be needed at all stages to act for the developer. Firstly to acquire the site and report on the title. He will establish whether there are for example cables or sewers which have easements that can materially or adversely affect the position of buildings on the site. Clearly if a mains sewer or fibre optic cables run diagonally under the land then much of the developable area will be sterilized and therefore the land will be worth less than a 'clean' site. Many sites today may be affected by wires for cable television.

Secondly the solicitor will need to advise in the preparation of leases for the tenant who will occupy the factory. In better times these leases will be 25 year term with 5 year upward only rent review clauses on fully repairing and insuring leases. Since the recession the developer will be more flexible and the tenant may be able to negotiate less onerous terms.

The solicitor will need to be fully up to date on case law and its effect on rent reviews and therefore ultimately on the value of the investment which is to be created. The lease will also need to be well drafted to take into account the good management of the estate, looking after common parts, insurance and other similar matters. It should not be so onerous that tenants refuse to sign it, but it should be fair and acceptable to the institution who may ultimately own the estate. Lastly the solicitor will need to advise in respect of the sale of the completed development. He will act against the solicitor representing the purchaser of the scheme - most probably a pension fund - and will need to consider any actions after the sale for example, any claims to his client in respect of collateral warranties, or rental guarantees on the leases.

The architect

The agent and the developer will have their own views on trying to secure as large a building as possible on the site in order to maximize the profit. The architect may bring a sense of reality to their aspirations. He will consider the ground conditions, easements, retaining walls, rights of light, highways access, car-parking and turning areas for commercial vehicles, local planning regulations (which differ throughout the country). He will then prepare a drawing of a workable industrial estate. He will consult the agent on what the market currently requires as well as what the investors prefer.

For example, on our imaginary three acre site it would be possible to build up to 60,000 sq. ft. Should the architect design for example two straight forward terraces, each of 30,000 sq. ft. facing each other across a common forecourt and easily divisible into units of say 5,000 sq. ft? Should he design say three detached buildings of varying sizes for example 10,000 sq. ft., 20,000 sq. ft., 30,000 sq. ft?

Should he develop part of the site and hold some of the land back for a pre-let? After considering these matters his appraisal will then be presented to the developer and agent for discussion prior to applying for outline planning permission and building regulations.

The quantity surveyor

After establishing the layout, the agent and his developer client will require some costs before being able to value the site or establish the likely profit. The quantity surveyor can discuss with the agent and the architect the specification which is required, and the type of building which is proposed. Is it for owner occupation or does it need to satisfy the funds requirements? The standards can vary considerably.

The developer may build, for example, to a higher specification for a fund than for an end-user. The quantity surveyor will then provide his estimate of the cost of building for the completed development not only for the building itself but also including all external works and sub-ground works. The quantity surveyor may require individual expert input in respect of engineering works, mechanical and electrical work.

Optional players/reserves

It may be necessary to have in reserve some experts in particular disciplines. These may include mechanical/electrical engineers, an expert to report on ground conditions, contaminated ground and soil surveys, a demolition expert to clear the site and grub out any foundations, a planning surveyor in the event that the planning application may end up going to appeal, a highways expert to report on any difficult traffic control or high generation of traffic, or a tax expert to advise in respect of VAT or other tax matters.

Funds adviser

In the event that the development is to be forward funded, the fund may require their own adviser to be involved at the commencement of the development in order to monitor the quality and the progress of the scheme. In the particular model chosen it has been assumed that the development will be built speculatively and that it will be sold on completion and therefore the funds adviser does not play a part in the original professional team.

The development

Having appointed the team the developer has now bought the 3 acre site and has obtained planning permission and building regulations for 60,000 sq. ft. of new industrial/warehouse units. The clock is ticking and interest is being levied in full on the site, acquisition fees and any other costs he has incurred such as planning and building regulation fees.

He must now begin to move quickly and confidently to progress the scheme within the original programme. His quantity surveyors will go out to tender for the building works or will negotiate a contract with one of several known builders in order to agree the building contract within a short timescale. The developer can now start work on the site. Simultaneously, the agent will commence his marketing to get tenants for the units as quickly as possible in order to minimize the void period at the completion of the scheme.

His marketing will include preparation of brochures, erection of a signboard, a full advertising campaign in the local and national press and professional journals, as well as targeted mailshots to those companies most likely to produce a tenant. It may also be prudent towards completion of the project to hold a reception for local dignitaries, agents and the press in order to raise an awareness of the scheme. The agent should not be advising his client to accept the first tenant who wants to sign the lease because clearly the quality of the tenant and his 'covenant' is of paramount importance to the value of the completed investment.

Earlier reference was made under the heading *The Quantity Surveyor* to the valuation of the site or the profit which the developer was expecting to make. A simple appraisal has been set out where the costs are known and the site is sold to the developer at £500,000. Each point is itemized and the purpose of the exercise is to establish the surplus left over which represents the developer's profit. In this particular development he is aiming for a 20% return on his total costs.

Project details

Scheme:	Manchester
Client:	Roker Developments
Tenure:	Freehold
Date:	7/4/93
Reference:	BOH

Investment value £

1. Industrial warehouse - 60,000 sq.ft
2. Rent - £4.25 per sq.ft
   Total rent 60,000 x £4.25   255,000
3. Less ground rent   -

Net estimated rental value   £   <u>255,000</u>

		£	£
4. Year purchase - in perpetuity @ 8.5% =		11,765	
Gross value (£255,000 x 11.7647)		3,000,000	
5. Purchaser's costs - 2.75%		80,292	
Net investment value	£	2,919,708	

Expenditure

Site purchase

		£	£
6. Site cost		500,000	
7. Acquisition fees	2.75%	13,750	
8. VAT on both above costs	17½%	89,906	

Pre-development costs

		£	£
9. Site survey		5,000	
10. Planning fees		2,500	
11. Demolition		10,000	
VAT on above costs	17½%	3,063	624,219

Construction costs

		£	£
12. Building costs 60,000 sq.ft. @ £25.00		1,500,000	
13. Design fees	12%	180,000	
14. Contingency	3%	50,400	
15. Building regulation fee		4,000	
16. Fund supervision fee		-	
VAT on above costs	17½%	303,520	2,037,920

Marketing costs

		£	£
17. Letting percentage of estimated rental value	15%	38,250	
18. Brochure and marketing		15,000	
19. Agent's sale fees % of net investment value	1.5%	43,796	
20. Legal sale fee % of net investment value	0.5%	14,599	
VAT on above costs	17½%	19,538	131,183
Carried forward	£		2,793,322

Brought forward		£	2,793,322

Finance

21. Finance rate	8%		
22. Site and pre-development costs			
100% for 15 months		62,222	
23. Construction and design costs			
50% for 9 months		<u>52,032</u>	114,254

Void Finance

24. On estimated rental value for 3 months		<u>63,750</u>
	£	<u>2,971,326</u>

25. VAT calculated on all costs 17½%

Total development costs		2,971,326
26. VAT refund		<u>519,982</u>
	£	<u>2,451,344</u>

Total development costs (net of VAT)

27. Surplus	(£2,919,708 - £2,451,344)	£	<u>468,364</u>

Summary

Net investment value	£2,919,708
Site value	£500,000
Surplus	£468,364
Surplus on total costs	19.11%
Yield on cost	10.40%

N.B. Some of the above figures may have suffered from slight distortion due to rounding off.

Item 1.   The gross building area is 60,000 sq.ft.

Item 2.   £4.25 per sq.ft. represents the estimated rental value.

Item 3.   The site is freehold and therefore no ground rent needs to be deducted.

Item 4. The agent and his developer believe that 8.5% yield is appropriate for this type of development.

Item 5. The investor who ultimately acquires the development will have his own costs, i.e. agents, solicitors, stamp duty, and will therefore require to deduct these from the gross development value to provide him with his net investment value.

Item 6. Site Cost - £500,000 is the figure at which the site can be bought in the open market.

Item 7. The developer will have his own acquisition costs being agents, solicitors and stamp duty.

Item 8. VAT is charged on all costs in accordance with recent legislation but is recovered by the developer throughout the scheme.

Item 9. It is likely that the developer will need a survey of the site.

Item 10. The scheme is fairly straight forward and no costs have been allowed for a planning appeal. Therefore the planning fees are reasonably nominal.

Item 11. There is a solid structure on the site and therefore an allocation of £10,000 has been made for demolition, clearance and grubbing out of foundations.

Item 12. At competitive tender the developer and his quantity surveyor believe that £25.00 per sq.ft. is a fair building price. No differential is made between the 60,000 sq.ft. in the investment value and the 60,000 sq.ft. in terms of building costs. If this was an office building then one would allow of the order of 85% from a gross to net area.

Item 13. Design fees are made up of architects, quantity surveyors and engineers and would be of the order of 12% of the estimated building cost. Many builders today include these fees within their quoted price when tendering for the building contract.

Item 14. Contingency - an allowance has been made of 3% for contingencies, that is any unknowns which are found during construction.

Item 15. Over and above planning permission, building regulations are required and an allocation of £4,000 has been made.

Item 16. As explained earlier in the chapter the development has now been forward funded and therefore the fund has no supervision fee in this particular scheme.

Item 17. The developer has decided to bring in a joint agent. For sole agency the fee would be 10% of 1 years full rental value. However in this case with a joint agent the fee will be 15% and the developer hopes that by having 2 firms letting the units he will secure good quality tenants much sooner.

Item 18. The joint agents will have a budget of £15,000 for brochure, boards and advertising.

Item 19. When the development is completed and let, the agent will sell the development to an investor and his fee will be 1.5% of the net investment value.

Item 20. A solicitor will be required to draw up the contract on behalf of the developer when selling to the investor and his fees will be of the order of 0.5%.

Item 21. The developer is able to secure interest at 2% above base rate.

Item 22. The developer must pay the full rate of interest on the site and his costs. Fifteen months has been taken which is made up of say 3 months between owning the site and obtaining planning permission, building regulations and commencing construction, a construction period of 9 months to complete the development, and a further 3 months post-completion for letting and selling the investment.

Item 23. During the 9 month construction period the costs of building together with all the design costs will attract interest on a cash flow basis. In other words, not all of the money is outstanding for the entire period but part of the money is outstanding part of the time. A simplistic view has been taken that 50% of the total monies will be outstanding for the whole 9 months building period.

Item 24. Three months has been allowed for void finance. This is a calculated decision in that the development is in a prime part of Manchester and should let very quickly but an allowance must be made either for a void period or by way of offering a rent free incentive to an in-coming tenant.

Item 25. VAT. As mentioned earlier in the chapter VAT is levied in accordance with the regulations but is fully recovered during and after the development period.

Item 26. As above.

Item 27. The surplus or "what is left for profit" represents 19.11% of total costs which is almost what the developer was looking for.

Professional fees

Architects' fees

The Royal Institute of British Architects (RIBA) no longer publish fee scales to cover its members' activities. However, the following table is an indication of current charges but fees should be negotiated with each individual architect or practice. The range of the percentages reflects the complexity of each separate job e.g. from simple sheds to buildings with quality finishings.

New work

Value of contract £	Fee as percentage of contract value %
50,000	7.20 - 9.75
100,000	6.50 - 8.80
150,000	6.20 - 8.45
250,000	5.85 - 8.00
750,000	5.30 - 7.30
1,000,000	5.25 - 7.25
2,000,000	5.15 - 7.05
5,000,000	5.05 - 7.00

Work to existing buildings

50,000	10.55 - 14.10
100,000	9.75 - 13.15
150,000	9.30 - 12.60
250,000	8.85 - 12.00
750,000	8.20 - 11.15
1,000,000	8.10 - 11.00
2,000,000	7.80 - 10.70
5,000,000	7.75 - 10.50

For works less than £20,000 and over £5 million the architect should agree the fee basis at the time of the appointment.

In addition to the above percentage fees, all expenses and disbursements for printing, models, photographs, travelling expenses, cost of postage, telephone calls and fax messages will be reimbursed where properly incurred in connection with the appointment. Alternatively a percentage addition or lump sum may be agreed.

Quantity surveyors' fees

The following worked examples of fees are based upon information contained in *Professional Charges for Quantity Surveying Services* price £9.70 (including postage) obtainable from Surveyors Publications, Surveyor Court, Westwood Way, Coventry CV4 8JE (0203 694757). It should be noted that these scales are recommended not mandatory.

Scales 36 and 37 - Building work

There are three basic categories of works

Category A. Complex with little repetition

Category B. Less complex with some repetition

Category C. Simple

and two basic scales of fees

1. Inclusive scale for complete service - Scale 36

2. Itemized scale divided into pre- and post-contract services - Scale 37

Worked examples of the percentages and actual fees are shown below.

Scale 36 Inclusive services

Value of Work £	Cat. A £	%	Cat. B £	%	Cat. C £	%
150,000	9,380	6.25	9,060	6.04	7,650	5.10
250,000	14,380	5.75	13,760	5.50	11,750	4.70
350,000	19,030	5.44	18,060	5.16	15,450	4.41
450,000	23,330	5.18	21,960	4.88	18,750	4.17
750,000	34,880	4.65	32,010	4.27	27,450	3.66

Value of Work £	Cat. A £ %	Cat. B £ %	Cat. C £ %
1,250,000	51,880 4.15	46,010 3.68	39,950 3.20
2,500,000	90,380 3.62	79,010 3.16	68,200 2.73
4,000,000	133,380 3.33	116,010 2.90	99,200 2.48

Scale 37 Pre-contract services

Value of Work £	Cat. A £ %	Cat. B £ %	Cat. C £ %
150,000	4,730 3.15	4,410 2.94	3,930 2.62
250,000	7,030 2.81	6,410 2.56	5,730 2.29
350,000	9,080 2.59	8,160 2.33	7,230 2.07
450,000	10,880 2.42	9,660 2.15	8,430 1.87
750,000	15,830 2.11	13,560 1.81	11,580 1.54
1,250,000	23,330 1.87	19,060 1.52	16,080 1.29
2,500,000	39,080 1.56	31,810 1.27	26,330 1.05
4,000,000	56,080 1.40	45,810 1.15	37,330 0.93

Scale 37 Post-contract services (overall charges - Alternative 1)

Value of Work £	Cat. A £ %	Cat. B £ %	Cat. C £ %
150,000	3,150 2.10	3,150 2.10	2,520 1.68
250,000	4,850 1.94	4,850 1.94	4,020 1.61
350,000	6,500 1.86	6,450 1.84	5,470 1.56
450,000	8,100 1.80	7,950 1.77	6,870 1.53
750,000	12,450 1.66	11,850 1.58	10,620 1.42
1,250,000	18,950 1.52	17,350 1.39	16,120 1.29

Scale 37 Post-contract services (overall
charges - Alternative 1) (cont'd)

Value of Work £	Cat. A £ %	Cat. B £ %	Cat. C £ %
2,500,000	34,200 1.37	30,100 1.20	27,870 1.11
4,000,000	51,200 1.28	44,100 1.10	40,370 1.01

For negotiating and agreeing
prices with a contractor

Value of work £	Fee £ %
150,000	750 0.50
250,000	1,050 0.42
350,000	1,350 0.39
450,000	1,650 0.37
750,000	2,400 0.32
1,250,000	3,350 0.27
2,500,000	4,600 0.18
4,000,000	6,100 0.15

Scale 38 Civil Engineering Works

Category I - Runways, roads, railways and earthworks and dredging and
monolithic walls.

Category II- Piled quay walls, suspended jetties, bridges, sewers,
storage and treatment tanks, turbine halls, reactor blocks.

Pre-contract services

Value of Work £	Cat. I Fee £ %	Cat. II Fee £ %
500,000	1,960 0.65	3,650 0.73
750,000	2,790 0.37	5,100 0.68

Value of Work £	Cat. I Fee £	%	Cat. II Fee £	%
1,500,000	5,040	0.34	8,850	0.59
2,500,000	7,540	0.30	12,850	0.51
5,000,000	12,790	0.26	21,850	0.44
7,000,000	16,790	0.24	28,850	0.41
12,000,000	25,790	0.21	45,350	0.38
15,000,000	30,290	0.20	54,350	0.36
25,000,000	44,790	0.18	83,350	0.33

Post-contract services

Value of Work £	Cat. I Fee £	%	Cat. II Fee £	%
500,000	5,950	1.19	10,750	2.15
750,000	8,250	1.10	15,000	2.00
1,500,000	14,250	0.95	26,250	1.75
2,500,000	20,750	0.83	38,250	1.53
5,000,000	34,000	0.68	65,250	1.31
7,000,000	44,000	0.63	86,250	1.23
12,000,000	68,000	0.57	135,750	1.13
15,000,000	81,500	0.54	162,750	1.09
25,000,000	125,000	0.50	249,750	1.00

Consulting engineers' fees

The Association of Consulting Engineers have always been responsible for the production of engineers' fee scales but these are less applicable than ever today because of the activities of the Monopolies Commission. Indeed, the next issue of the Conditions of Engagement for Consulting Engineers will not carry any fee guidance at all.

Engineers' fees today are calculated by dividing the Cost of the Works by the Output Price Index and the resultant figure is then applied to a graph to show the percentage to be applied to the final cost of the works. Full details can be obtained from The Association of Consulting Engineers, Alliance House, 12 Caxton Street, London SW1H 0QZ (Tel: 071-222 6557)

Landscape consultants' fees

Fees on the percentage basis

The following is a precis of the Landscape Institute Conditions of Engagement and Professional Charges. It should be noted that the fees are recommended and not mandatory.

Remuneration on the percentage basis (contracts over £10,000)

The fee is in two parts:

Part 1 is assessed from a graph which indicates the fee percentage from 6% to 14% varying according to the value of the contract from £10,000 to in excess of £900,000.

Part 2 is a coefficient ranging from 1.0 where the consultant has overall responsibility to his client for a normal balance of 'hard' and 'soft' works. This may increase to 1.2 when the 'soft' works element exceeds 50% of the landscape contract or for private garden contracts.The coefficient may be decreased to 0.8 for other types of jobs such as golf courses and road landscaping.

Example

Assume a project which has a contract value of £100,000 including both 'hard' and 'soft' works in a new business park.

The fee graph shows that the percentage 'norm' is 7.5%
Coefficient for soft works element exceeds 50% = 1.2
Job coefficient is 1.0
Compounded coefficient 1.0 x 1.2
Total percentage fee is 7.5% x 1.2 = 9.0%
Fee to be charged is 9.0% of £100,000 = £9,000

The scale of fees allows for other methods of remuneration such as lump sum fees, using a ceiling figure in conjunction with a time basis or having a retainer which can be reviewed after a period and paid according to actual work carried out or allowed to stand in full.

Similarly when only occasional work is required this can be carried out on a time basis.

If Bills of Quantities are required these would normally be charged at RICS scale Category C. Site surveys would normally be paid on a lump sum basis of estimated time involved. Disbursements would of course be charged at cost and include normal out-of-pocket expenses.

Professional team 'all-in' fees

Assessing the fees for a professional team working on a development project can be complicated due to the different methods of fee calculation adopted by the various professional bodies. Worked examples of these are shown in this chapter related to a range of contract values. Sometimes one discipline is appointed 'lead professional' and an overall fee is agreed with the client for the whole team and the table below shows the effect of this arrangement. The figures have been rounded off to the nearest £1000.

Project Cost	8% £000	9% £000	10% £000	11% £000	12% £000	13% £000	14% £000	15% £000
200	16	18	20	22	24	26	28	30
300	24	27	30	33	36	39	42	45
400	32	36	40	44	48	52	56	60
500	40	45	50	55	60	65	70	75
600	48	54	60	66	72	78	84	90
700	56	63	70	77	84	91	98	105
800	64	72	80	88	96	104	112	120
900	72	81	90	99	108	117	126	135
1,000	80	90	100	110	120	130	140	150
1,200	96	108	120	132	144	156	168	180
1,400	112	126	140	154	168	182	196	210
1,600	128	144	160	176	192	208	224	240
1,800	144	162	180	198	216	234	252	270
2,000	160	180	200	220	240	260	280	300
2,250	180	202	225	247	270	292	315	337
2,500	200	225	250	275	300	325	350	375
2,750	220	247	275	302	330	357	385	412
3,000	240	270	300	330	360	390	420	450
3,250	260	292	325	357	390	422	455	487
3,500	280	315	350	385	420	455	490	525
3,750	300	337	375	412	450	487	525	562
4,000	320	360	400	440	480	520	560	600
4,500	360	405	450	495	540	585	630	675

Professional team 'all-in' fees (cont'd)

Project Cost	8% £000	9% £000	10% £000	11% £000	12% £000	13% £000	14% £000	15% £000
5,500	440	495	550	605	660	715	770	825
6,000	480	540	600	660	720	780	840	900
7,000	560	630	700	770	840	910	980	1050
8,000	640	720	800	880	960	1040	1120	1200
9,000	720	810	900	990	1080	1170	1260	1350
10,000	800	900	1000	1100	1200	1300	1400	1500

Indices have been used for many years in the construction industry, not only to assist in obtaining up to date estimates of cost but also in the 'formula method' of calculating the increase or decrease in costs on a contract.

The indices are also useful when projecting cash flow forecasts on a contract which may run over several years.

To use an index, one must have knowledge of the various indices published and select the most appropriate for the type of building or civil engineering work in the contract.

Care must be taken when using an index to update rates in a bill of quantities for the purpose of pricing an estimate, that the level of preliminaries relates precisely. If rates include preliminaries in the contract bills it is vital that the index applied also includes them.

By using the elemental cost analyses contained in Chapter 2 and selecting an appropriate index for the year/month/quarter a cost plan can be prepared which then could be applied to a new building based on the rate per square metre of each element.

The main source of indices for the quantity surveyor is the *Building Cost Information Service* (BCIS) which is published by the RICS. Other sources include the NEDO indices for the variation of price clauses prepared by the PSA and published by HMSO. Other important information on building costs and levels is stated in Spons Architects' and Builders Price Book (obtainable from E & F N Spon, 2-6, Boundary Row, London, SE1 8HN (071-865-0066).

The Civil Engineering industry under the ICE Conditions of Contract use a price adjustment formula (sometimes referred to as the Baxter formula) on jobs with a long construction period. This is based on fewer items of materials than the Building Cost indices and include the cost of:

1. Labour and supervision in civil engineering construction
2. Plant - cost of providing and maintaining constructional plant and equipment
3. Aggregates
4. Bricks and clay products
5. Cement
6. Cast iron pipes and fittings
7. Coated roadstone and bitumen products
8. Timber

    9. Fuel for plant
    10. Reinforcing steel and metal sections
    11. Structural steelwork

Construction costs are amounts paid by contractors for the labour employed, materials purchased, plant costs, rates, rent overheads and taxes.

  Construction cost indices are compiled by various authorities, institutions and quantity surveying practices; they are published periodically in journals and publications from HMSO. The figures are based on general building tenders deflated to measure changes in costs without any allowance for market trends.

  Tender level rates are the amounts charged to clients which fluctuate according to market trends. They increase when there is a large volume of work available and decrease during lean periods. The tender level rates are calculated indirectly from construction costs with the addition of the profit element. It has been known for contractors to put tender prices of nett cost without any addition for profit (and even less than nett) when a period of depression in the industry prevails, in order to keep the work force and plant occupied.

  Tender level indices are compiled from accepted tenders during a certain period, averaged and compared to a standard schedule.

  The following table shows a comparison between construction costs and tender levels during the period 1970 to 1994 (1993 and 1994 figures are estimated).

Year	Construction costs	Tender level rates
1970	100	100
1971	109	115
1972	119	145
1973	140	199
1974	166	237
1975	205	242
1976	241	241
1977	275	258
1978	299	299
1979	342	371
1980	410	458
1981	458	467
1982	506	453
1983	537	469
1984	569	495
1985	600	514
1986	631	540
1987	665	608
1988	706	728

1989	759	851
1990	812	766
1991	852	651
1992	877	637
1993	889 (E)	640 (E)
1994	920 (E)	603 (E)

From these figures it can be seen for example the depression in the industry in 1976 to 1978, 1982 to 1987 and 1989 onwards.

It should be mentioned here that PSA have other schedules of rates which are used for Measured Term Contracts and are updated each month by percentage adjustments, not indices. The statistical use of these may be of great use in updating items on maintenance contracts.

Other bodies such as British Telecom use the National Building Schedule which is independently produced.

The use of indices is simply explained as follows:-

1. take the index of the current year/month/quarter from the relevant table e.g. 1994 - 920

2. take the index of the year/month/quarter of the tender being updated e.g. 1987 - 665.

$$920 - 665 = 225$$

$$\frac{225}{665} \times 100 = \underline{38.35\%}$$

Rates to be increased by 38.35% for new project but adjustments for regional cost differences must also be considered (see Introduction).

Indices used in construction industry

Generally	BCIS Royal Institution of Chartered Surveyors 85/87, Clarence Street Kingston Upon Thames, Surrey KT1 1RB (081-546-7554)
DOE Public sector building tender price index published in *Housing and construction statistics*	HMSO

BCIS Building tender price index	Davis, Langdon and
BCIS General building cost index	Everest, Tender price
	index, published in Spon's
	price books.

It should be noted that other indices relevent to the construction industry are printed in the following books published by E & FN Spon:

Spon's Architects' and builders' price book
Spon's Civil engineering price book
Spon's Landscape and external works price book
Spon's Mechanical and electrical services price book

Property insurance

Rebuilding costs for insurance

It is essential that property owners have adequate insurance cover their property and this section is intended to show how the sum to be covered can be assessed quickly. The easiest way to achieve this is by using the square metre prices in Chapter 1 as a base.

The appropriate rate should be multiplied by the area of the building to be insured. The resultant figure must then be adjusted by applying both the historical indices in chapter 15 and the regional variation factor in the Introduction.

The insurance cover must also include for the demolition of the damaged building (not just clearing away debris but grubbing existing foundations and basements) and professional fees to plan and supervise the work of reconstruction.

Example

Pre-war office block, original cost unknown; total loss

	£
Present day cost:	
Office block - 4,000 square metres @ £900m2 (see chapter 1)	3,600,000
Add 5% for geographical variation	180,000
Allowance for period for redesign, obtaining permissions, tendering etc.	3,780,000
2 years @ 5½% p.a.	588,263
	4,167,450
Assuming 18 month building contract with predicted inflation @ 5% p.a. (9 months)	156,279
Carried forward	£ 4,323,729

Brought forward		£ 4,323,729
Allowance for demolition of old building		200,000
		£ 4,523,729
Allowance for professional fees	12%	542,847
		£ 5,066,576
Add VAT	17½%	886,650
Required insurance cover		£ 5,953,226
	say	£ 6,000,000

If the original building costs were known (i.e. the costs would be available if the property was constructed recently) the present day costs would be calculated by applying indices to the original building cost figures to bring them up to date and using the cost per square metre method as above.

Index